W9-CDE-176

TRADECRAFT

for the church on mission

WORKBOOK

Tradecraft Workbook

978-0-9961847-4-8

Printed in the United States of America

Book design by Rachel Allen rachel@rachelallencreative.com

Author Profiles

Rodney Calfee: Rodney has been in leadership in the local church for more than twenty years, including an urban church plant in Birmingham, Alabama. In 2010 he began writing, editing, and consulting for The Upstream Collective. He is also a co-author of *Tradecraft: For the Church on Mission*. Rodney is currently the Content Leader for the International Mission Board.

Larry E. McCrary: Larry is the co-founder and Executive Director of The Upstream Collective. He and his family have lived abroad for the last 15 years in Europe where he has served in a variety of strategy and leadership roles. Prior to moving to Europe he was a church planter and pastor in the US. He is a co-author of T*radecraft: For the Church on Mission* and *First 30 Daze: Practical Encouragement for Living Abroad Intentionally*. He and his wife live in Louisville where he serves as Pastor of International Missions at Sojourn Community Church East.

Caleb Crider: Caleb is the co-founder of The Upstream Collective. In 2002 he and his family moved to Spain, leading a team of church planters focused on art, social action, and culture exchange. He is a co-author of *Tradecraft: For the Church on Mission*. Caleb currently lives in Richmond, Virginia, where he leads Instructional Design for the International Mission Board.

Wade Stephens: Wade has lived on mission with his family for 10 years in Eastern Europe. For the past several years, he has been in the U.S. while helping churches, companies, and individuals that are seeking to live as missionaries. Working as a missionary and/or tentmaker over the years, he recognizes an opportunity for the gospel to advance through creative endeavors.

Zach Bradley: The Upstream Collective, Editor.

Introduction

Since the release of *Tradecraft* in February of 2013, we have been asked by a number of churches and organizations for a method of group study utilizing the *Tradecraft: For the Church on Mission* material. This resource is designed to fill that request, and we believe it can be a valuable resource in a variety of ways. During the production period, the material was tested by many churches and other groups who utilized it as training materials to prepare their people for mission.

Here are a few settings in which the workbook has been successfully used thus far:

Discipleship Groups - Discipleship is at the core of *Tradecraft*, and it can be used as a part of your regular discipleship process, whether Sunday School classes, small groups, or any other group discipleship format. *Tradecraft* helps the disciple learn practical ways to live out the Great Commission, an important part of following Christ.

Training Church Members for Local Missions - The tools in *Tradecraft* are employed regularly in overseas mission, but they can be just as fruitful in local mission. If you want to impact the local community with the gospel, you have to know the culture found therein. This workbook will walk your local mission teams through employing missionary tools in their own neighborhoods.

Church Planting Core Team - Planting a healthy church also requires an intimate knowledge of the people and place into which it will be rooted. Walk through this workbook with your team and learn your city and its people well.

Other uses we have seen:

- Short Term Mission Trips Training
- Training in Churches and Colleges Sending out Study Abroad Students
- Long-term Missionary Training Schools
- Personal Study
- Neighborhood or Community Bible Study Groups
- Family Study and Training Tool

We believe this information belongs in the hands of every believer and can be walked through with any group that simply wants to more effectively engage in mission in their own neighborhoods or around the world.

We hope you enjoy the book and find it both meaningful and helpful!

Larry E. McCrary

TABLE OF CONTENTS

8	WEEK ONE: THINKING LIKE A MISSIONARY
30	WEEK TWO: ACTING LIKE A MISSIONARY
54	WEEK THREE: FOLLOWING THE SPIRIT
80	WEEK FOUR: MAPPING
102	WEEK FIVE: EXEGETING THE CULTURE
127	WEEK SIX: BUILDING RELATIONSHIPS
158	WEEK SEVEN: IDENTIFYING PERSONS OF PEACE
190	WEEK EIGHT: ENGAGING TRIBES
217	WEEK NINE: CONTEXTUALIZATION
245	WEEK TEN: PURSUING ALTERNATIVE PATHS
267	WEEK ELEVEN: PROTECTING INDIGINEITY
296	WEEK TWELVE: GROUP DISCUSSION

Week One: day 1

Thinking Like a Missionary

I'm Not a Missionary. Wait ... Am I?

You live in a neighborhood in a city or town or one of its suburbs, and you work in an office all day and go home to your family and friends at night. You drive an SUV, mini-van, or station wagon during the week, but you look forward to riding your motorcycle or bicycle, going to the park with your kids, or visiting a friend's house on the weekend. The people around you are similar to you. They may be different colors, or from different places, but their lives look fairly similar to yours. You may go to the same college, send your kids to the same school, work in the same office, or cheer for the same teams. You pass them as you drive out of your neighborhood to worship with your church every Sunday morning, and you pray they would know and follow Jesus. Throughout the week, you look for opportunities to be with your friends and neighbors and show them the love and character of Christ.

Does this short description (or some variation thereof) describe you?

Think about the description of the life of the person above—about your life. Is this a missionary's life? Does the previous paragraph describe a missionary? If so, what about the life described above says "missionary?" If not, what is missing?

Activity

Define "missionary." Give 3 examples of people who fit your definition of missionary. List the things about them that make them missionaries. Is it certain things they do? Character traits? Relationships? What makes them missionaries?

	A missionary is:
1	

	A missionary is: cont.
2	
3	

	Scripture
1	What does the Bible say about missionaries? What specific passages do you know of that define who they are and what they do? How do those passages shape your definition of a missionary?

#	Homework due:________
1	Watch this video: **https://www.youtube.com/watch?v=e_4VoVo3svM** How common would you say the views of missionaries expressed by the children in the video is? Do you hear echoes of your own description of missionaries in their words? Are their descriptions right?
2	By your own definition, are you a missionary? Explain.
3	Perform a Google search for descriptions/definitions of missionaries. They are everywhere on the internet. List a couple you agree with and a couple that you find lacking. How do they differ from your own definition?
4	Pray for God to help you set aside preconceptions and be open to new (yet ancient) ideas as you seek Him and His direction through Scripture, study, and prayer.

Week One: day 2

Who Are the Missionaries, Really?

Missionaries are traditionally thought of as people who move somewhere away from home to take the gospel to people who have not yet heard or experienced it. There is a very literal idea of "sent-ness" inherent in the role. They take up residence in a new culture, may have to learn a new language, adopt new dress codes, eat weird things, and take on new cultural norms. Missionaries, by traditional standards, are sent. They are professional Christians paid by the church or an organization to take the gospel to faraway places.

But aren't all believers sent?

Sent-ness

Read John 20:21.

In this verse, Jesus was speaking to the disciples after His resurrection and not long before His ascension. He was preparing them for His departure and the fact that they would be picking up where He was leaving off. "In the same way the Father sent me," He said, "I am sending you." Jesus was sent. In the same way, He sent/sends His followers to carry on the same mission for which He was sent.

Read 1 Peter 2:9-12.

Peter wrote this letter to all of the Christians dispersed (exiles-1:1) in a few particular areas—ALL of the Christians, not just a few. They were dispersed because of persecution, and he told them how to live as exiles and sojourners. They were not a random smattering of individuals, but a chosen people—a priesthood—with a purpose. They were there to "proclaim the excellencies of Him who called them out of darkness." They were to live in such a way that the Gentiles around them recognized a different character in them and glorified God because of it. They were there for a purpose, with a mission. They were missionaries. All of them. And in these new places, they were working jobs and building homes and lives among the people. They weren't all full-time paid Christian workers. They were regular people with regular jobs, but they had a heavenly identity. They were strangers and pilgrims, not only because they were out of their hometowns, but also because they were actually citizens of another kingdom and longing for home. Their work there was to live out the character of the kingdom and King whose return they were awaiting.

Read Hebrews 11:13-16.

The writer of Hebrews makes clear again that those who died in faith were looking for a home. They were exiles, sent by God with a purpose (11:8). Had they simply been longing and living for the home from whence they came, they could have returned, he says. They were looking for a "better country, a heavenly one."

Read 2 Corinthians 5.

Paul addressed the same topic with the Corinthian church in this passage (to ALL of the believers there). Verses 1-10 deal with the nature of our bodies. They are a tent, he says, which means they are temporary. We long for something more permanent, more perfect. But while we are here, compelled by the love of Christ, we faithfully work to persuade others of the rule and reign of God (v. 11-15). Everything is different than it was. We have come to Christ, and He has made all things new. We are new creations. We don't even refer to one another in the same terms any longer. Our identity has changed, and Paul gives us a common name: ambassador. That's who we are, we who follow Christ. We are ambassadors of a different kingdom imploring the people to whom we have been sent to be reconciled to God (16-20). We are all missionaries.

#	Questions
1	After reading these passages, does your definition of a missionary change from Day 1? How so?
2	Who is a missionary?

#	Questions, cont.
3	What does a missionary do?

#	Homework due:__________
1	Whether you believe it yet or not, if you follow Jesus, you are a missionary. You have joined in God's mission and are called to live out the character of His kingdom in the times and places He has sent you. Think about your life, your daily schedule. What keeps you from living like a missionary where you are? What do you need that you do not have to be an ambassador and implore those around you to be reconciled to God? How can you be a better missionary?
2	**Prayerfully** read back through the Scripture passages again and ask God to apply His Word to your heart so that you may understand the fullness of your identity in Christ (Ephesians 1:17-23). Take time to listen as you pray, and ask the Lord to give you insight and clarity into who you are.

Week One: day 3

Something Is Broken.

Most Western Christians do not think of themselves as missionaries, and there is a reason we don't. We've not been taught to. In fact, we have taught and been taught quite the opposite. Christian culture has said missionaries are somewhere "out there." The people who make up the churches "here" are merely "lay people" who can evangelize, but that is somehow different than mission. The way most Western churches are structured, lay people are taught and encouraged to invite friends to come hear the "professionals" (pastors, evangelists, and missionaries) preach the gospel. They are taught to focus on self-growth and sanctification, but they are not typically invited to join in the mission in a more meaningful way. Their God-given identity as sent-ones is stifled, and they begin to merely fill the pews and attend the programs of the church instead of going on mission in the daily rhythms of their lives. This is a broken system in need of repair.

What's Wrong with the System?

The system perpetuated by many churches is hierarchical and divided. It includes three types of people: lay people, pastors and other church leaders, and missionaries. Commitment level of the individual is seen according to the level he reaches in the hierarchy. All Christians are meant to serve in the church, but there are those called specifically to serve as leaders. They become pastors and lead churches of lay people. They are committed, but the pinnacle of commitment comes in the form of the missionary:

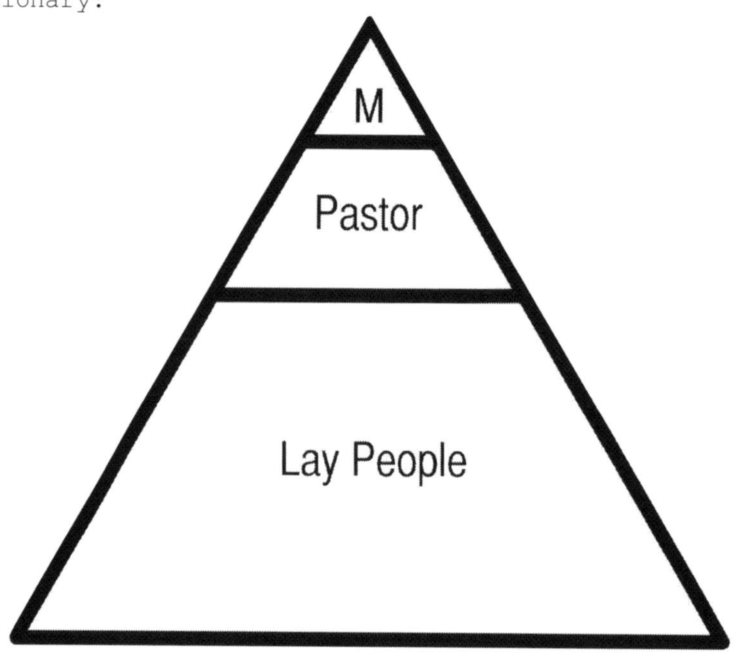

The following are problems that have arisen out of this model. Discuss how these issues might affect the daily lives of the different types of people. How might it affect their own personal relationships with the Lord? How might these issues affect their local churches as a whole and the impact they have on the local community and the world?

1. A false identity is created for lay people—they don't know they are missionaries. The expectations set for them in the church are low, and the opportunities to engage people on mission are few, highly programmatic, and largely focused inward.
2. A false identity is created for pastors and missionaries. Since their perceived commitment is higher, they are expected to be "superhero" Christians. Unobtainable goals and expectations are set for them, and the lion's share of the work of the church rests on their shoulders.

#	Homework due:__________
1	**Pray.** It is difficult when we see problems within our churches. Often our immediate responses are quick and rash and unhelpful. They can actually be divisive, which in turn can be deadly for our churches. Pray James 1:5. Humbly ask God for wisdom for yourself and your church. He gives generously to those who ask. Whether you are a lay person, pastor, or missionary according to this traditional understanding, ask the Lord how you might live more like a missionary—an ambassador of His kingdom—and encourage others to do the same. Imagine if instead of the hierarchical understanding presented, we thought of everyone in our churches as missionaries. Some missionaries are gifted and called to lead our churches as pastors/elders by equipping others for the mission to which they are called. Some missionaries are called and sent to live in foreign contexts. And still others (the vast majority) are called to live as missionaries (read: sent-ones) right where God has placed them already. What if the entirety of our churches understood and lived out our missionary identities? So much about our churches would necessarily change. Pray that God would help you understand how you are a missionary, and that He would use you to help others understand,

#	Homework, cont.
	as well. Take some time to write down your thoughts as you pray and listen to the Lord. If you are a pastor or other church leader, how might you better equip your church as missionaries? If you are a "missionary," how might you serve your church and help them understand what it is to be missionaries? How might you more faithfully engage with your local church? If you are a "lay person" how might you begin to be more involved? How might you also help to relieve some of the pressure on leaders and full-time missionaries in/from your local church? Consider each of these questions from your particular perspective. Take a little time to write out your answers.

Week One: day 4

Where Is the Church?

Every local church has its shortcomings. Certainly that is to be expected, because the church is comprised of imperfect, sinful people. Yet there are certainly many, many powerful and beautiful victories in the history of the church. Even within flawed modern structures, the gospel has been taught, missionaries have been sent, and many have heard and believed the gospel who otherwise would not have. But the manner in which the Western church in particular has carried out the mission had some unintended consequences. As the divide grew between "lay" people, church leadership, and missionaries (as discussed on Day 3), missionaries began to partner together to accomplish more for the mission. And they were successful in many ways over centuries of missionary work. Parachurch missionary organizations rose up and began carrying the burden of sending and caring for missionaries apart from local churches in many cases.

#	What's the Problem?
1	In your own words, is there an inherent problem with missionary agencies (parachurch ministries) taking the lead in sending? Is there anything vital missing from the process?

#	What's the Problem?, cont.
2	Read the Great Commission in Matthew 28:18-20. Now read Jesus' final recorded words to His followers just before His ascension in Acts 1:4-8. To whom is Jesus speaking, and why is it important to know His audience?

In each instance, Jesus was speaking to the remaining Apostles. The eleven (to be joined by Matthias and, eventually, Paul) would go on to birth and lead the early church. The churches they led are the same churches who sent and cared for missionaries throughout the Book of Acts and the rest of the New Testament. It was from local churches that missionaries were sent out (Acts 13:1-3) and to the local churches that they returned to share the stories of God's faithfulness (Acts 14:24-28; 18:22-23). It is the church that constantly cared for and prayed for those it sent out, looked for news from the field, and sent people and resources to minister to missionaries on their journeys (1 Corinthians 16:5-11; 2 Corinthians 1:11; Ephesians 6:21; Colossians 4:7-18). The responsibility to do all of these things was given by Jesus to the church (Matthew 28:18-20; John 20:21). It is important to see that the responsibility to send, care for, and serve alongside others belongs to the church, or, more specifically, to the local church from which they are sent. The church is strangely absent, however, from the most common paths to mission followed by missionaries.

These are the pathways that are most commonly followed by individuals who feel called to mission:

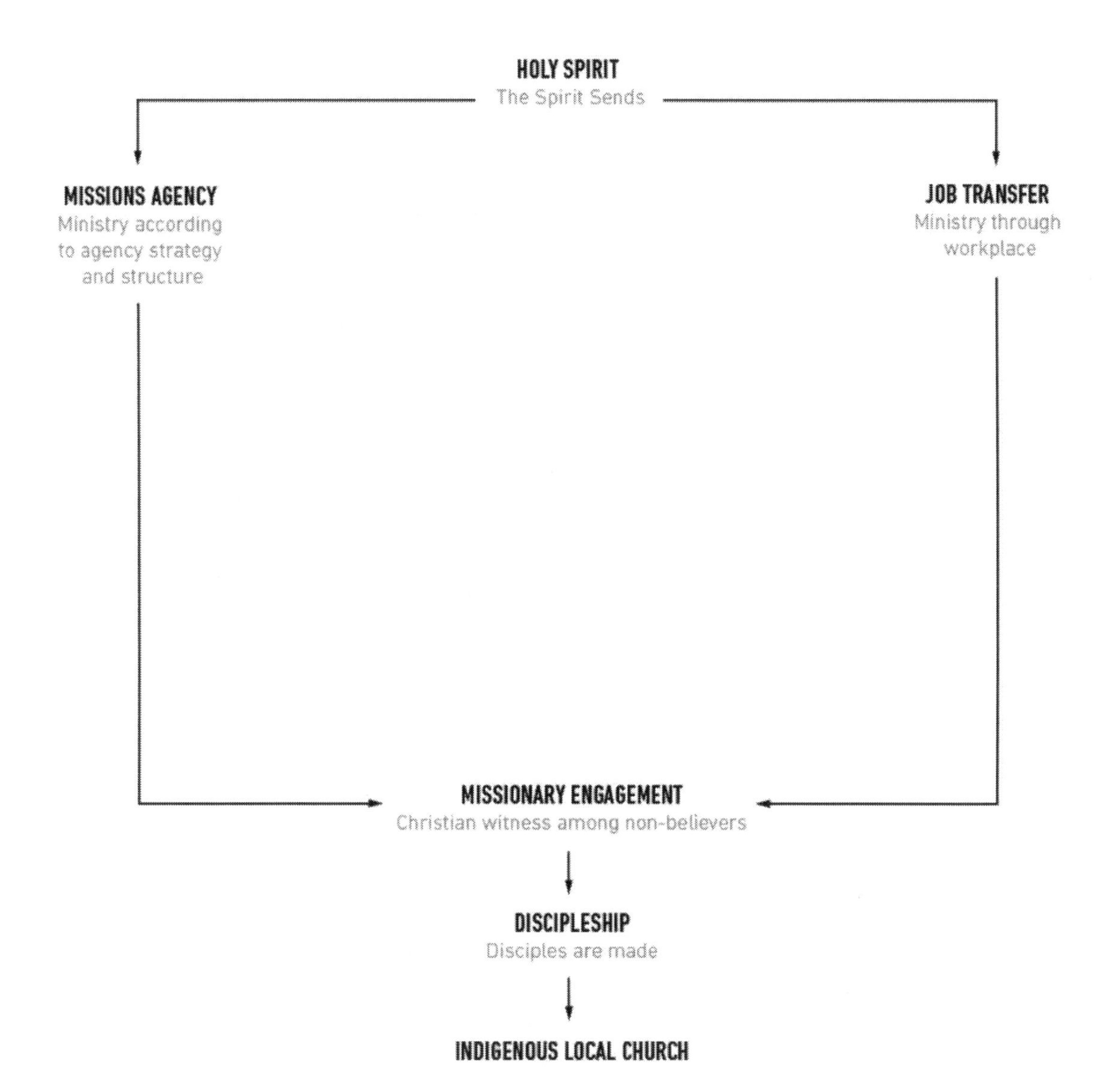

As you can see in the diagram, there are traditionally two main paths to the mission field—through a job transfer with an employer or through joining a missions agency. Either path can land the missionary on the field and lead to missionary engagement, disciple-making, and indigenous church plants. But where is the church in the process? Where is the authority for sending people out on God's mission? Is it important to note that God has always worked through a specific covenant people who represented Him among the nations? If so, who are God's covenant people now?

#	Homework due:__________
1	First, thoughtfully consider the questions on the previous page and give honest answers to each.
2	Think (and/or read) through the covenants made throughout the Scriptures, including the Abrahamic Covenant (Genesis 12:1-3), the Mosaic Covenant (Exodus 19-24), the Davidic Covenant (2 Samuel 7:5-16) and the New Covenant (Jeremiah 31:31-40; Luke 22:14-20). With whom did God make each of the covenants?

#	Homework, cont.
3	Were the promises and responsibilities of each meant for a certain people, or were they general promises and responsibilities meant for all people? Is the distinction important? Why?
4	In Matthew 16:18, for the first time recorded in the New Testament, Jesus named the people through whom He would carry out His mission in all the earth. He told Peter that the very gates of hell would not prevail against His church, the ones to whom He later sent the Holy Spirit to lead them with Christ's authority (John 16:7-15). Paul referred to this same Church as the body of Christ, with Christ as our head (Ephesians 1:22-23). Just as there has been throughout biblical history, there remains a single chosen covenant people, given authority as ambassadors to represent God in the earth. That covenant people is Christ's church. It is imperative that the church rediscover her role in sending God's people into the world as fully equipped ambassadors for the glory of God.

#	Activity
1	Do a Google search for "mission agency" or "mission organization." Search through the results and give a quick overview of a few of the organizations. For each one, answer one simple question: what is the role of the local church when partnering with this agency?
2	Is there a better way? Yes, there is. Christ has given authority to His church. Pray that the greater church and your local church, would understand and walk in that authority to equip missionaries as representatives of Christ in their homes, workplaces, neighborhoods, and around the world.

Week One: day 5

Lost Communication

If you have talked with many missionaries who have been on the field for an extended period of time, you have probably heard at least some of them (if not all) say they feel alone on the field. They feel as though they were sent out with an encouraging hug and all but forgotten within a few months' time. They may receive a periodic postcard or Skype call from someone back home, and they are asked to give an update on their work when they return stateside. On the whole, though, they are alone, separated from the local body of believers with whom they fellowshiped, worshiped, and served. What a tragedy to have been called and sent out from a particular body of believers only to be forgotten when the hard work on the field began.

Meanwhile, there is also a conversation going on among American churches about being missional. They are trying to figure out how to live and communicate the gospel within an ever-more quickly changing culture. Whether they would say it this way or not, they are trying to figure out how to cross cultures with the gospel. Isn't this what missionaries have been doing for centuries? Yet churches are trying to figure out how to do it without the input of the seasoned veterans. Churches are re-inventing the missionary wheel. Shouldn't churches talking about mission be inviting the input of "missionaries" on the field?

We Need Each Other

There is an answer. There is a better way. It is not new, but a return to a biblical prescription. Don't misunderstand, missionaries and mission agencies have worked hard and produced much fruit over their years of work. They have done and continue to do great work. However, there is some re-shaping and re-directing that needs to be done. The disconnect that has come as a result of the current missions model is woeful. The Church has outsourced the Great Commission and removed itself from God's global mission on a grand scale. This must change. We need each other.

The Great Commission, the sending authority given by Christ, was given to the church, and the church (local churches) bear the responsibility for it. Parachurch ministries are an incredible gift to the church, but only when they come alongside the church as they are meant to do ("para" means "beside"). Churches must once again take the lead in sending, directing, caring for, and joining their sent-out ones as they cross cultures with the gospel.

A Better Way

As was stated above, there is a better way. There is a way for the church to join in the work on the field and not leave her sent-out ones alone. There is a way for the church to learn from the experience of those it has sent:

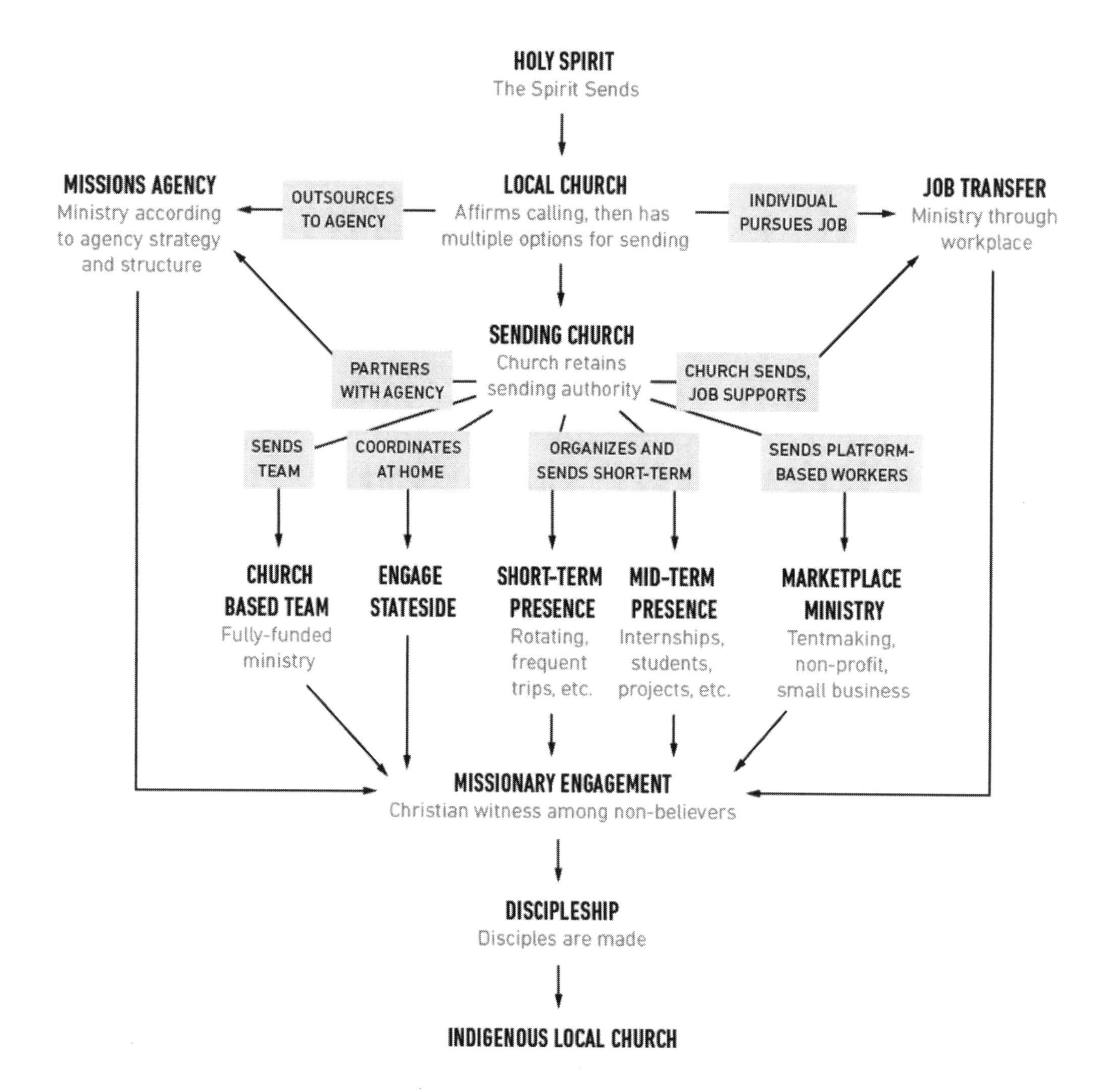

As you can see in the above diagram, the traditional paths to mission remain, but the local church retains the sending authority given by Christ. Moreover, those paths are two of many and can be applied not only to international mission, but also to all of the missionaries who remain in the neighborhoods and communities where God has already placed them. In each case above, the local church retains authority in the life of the ones sent and helps them determine how engagement will happen. The missionaries are loved and shepherded, and the local church reaps the wonderful benefits of learning from the members' experiences on the field. As a result, people in the local church become partners on the field and learn to think and act like the people they already are: missionaries.

#	**Homework** due:__________
1	In your own words, describe the main differences between the two "Paths to Mission" diagrams from Day 4 and Day 5.

#	Homework, cont.
2	What deficiencies are there in the former model? The latter? What deficiencies in the former are corrected in the latter? Are there deficiencies not addressed by the latter?
3	What are the benefits of a model like the latter to missionaries on the field? To the churches that send them?

#	Homework, cont.
4	**Pray** for God's church. Pray for your local church. Pray that we would be awakened to the weight and responsibility of the Great Commission. Pray that we would have our eyes opened to the necessity of the local church's involvement in equipping, sending, and continually caring for all of those whom the Lord has called together with us. Pray earnestly to the Lord of the harvest that He would send well-equipped workers into the harvest He has prepared (Matthew 9:38).

Week One: Questions for Group Discussion

#	Questions
1	Compare and contrast your definitions of "missionary." Talk about how your definitions may have changed from the beginning of the week to the end of the week.
2	What about a traditional understanding of missionaries is difficult to let go when we begin to think in terms of all Christ-followers being missionaries? What gives you pause when speaking of yourselves in missionary terms?
3	How might you as individuals and a group begin to think beyond the traditional hierarchical divisions within the church? How can you humbly help others begin to think and act differently, as well? Are there things that are already in place within your church to help you think differently about your role as an ambassador of Christ? Are there things that could be quickly/ easily shaped to begin the process?

#	Questions, cont.
4	Church leaders: how can you equip your church and expose their true identity to them? How can you encourage them to think and act like missionaries? "Lay people:" how can you relieve some of the pressure from your leadership to be super Christians? How can you help them carry the burden and responsibility of the Great Commission?
5	Discuss the two "Paths to Mission" diagrams. Discuss their deficiencies honestly, and talk about the differences in the two. What would it mean practically for a church to begin to view mission in these terms and to be responsible for the sending, care, and shepherding of those who are sent? What in the local church would necessarily change? Who would it take to make those changes?

Spend some time talking through and praying about the different approaches to sending people into mission. Talk honestly. Remember Scripture and read it. Pray that God would show you how your local body should endeavor to be on mission together. Pray for His grace, that you would walk in unity together as you discover His direction for your church.

Week Two: day 1

Acting Like a Missionary

	Field Training
1	Watch this short clip from the 2001 film Spy Game. http://www.youtube.com/watch?v=EhUNj85HfU4 How did master spy Nathan Muir (played by Robert Redford), train new recruit Tom Bishop (Brad Pitt's character)? How would you describe their relationship? How would Bishop's training have differed without Muir's help?

Tradecraft is the collection of knowledge that serves as the foundation of all artisan labor. The blacksmith maintains the strength of the material by plunging hot iron into cool water before re-heating the cooling metal. The finish carpenter uses a gauge rather than a tape to measure, because in woodworking, numbers rarely add up. The sailor can't help but notice the color of the sky at sunset; it forecasts the weather for the coming day. These are the skills that make the difference between mere workers and master craftsmen. The wisdom of experience informs everything that a tradesman does. This is why most trades, such as espionage in the example above, require apprenticeship.

#	Activity
1	Consider for a moment something that you're good at that you do fairly often. This can be anything—driving a car, making a sandwich, playing touch football. Now break down that activity into micro-skills. What goes into doing something that you're so familiar with?
2	Of the skills you listed above, which of the skills are unique to the task (meaning you rarely use them for anything else), and which are transferable (meaning that you use those same skills to accomplish other tasks)? Next to each skill, make a note of other possible applications.

#	**Homework** due:___________
1	Make a list of the basic "skills" involved in following Christ.
2	Which of the skills are most developed in your own life? Which are least developed?
3	What are some ways you might be able to strengthen your weaker skills?

#	Homework, cont.
4	What Christ-following skills have you learned by experience rather than study?
5	How are you passing your Christ-following skills on to someone else?
6	Have you ever been on a mission trip? Did you feel like you were participating in God's mission in a meaningful way?

#	Scripture
1	Read Matthew 4:18-22, the account of Jesus calling His first disciples. To what did Christ call the Twelve?
2	How do you think the disciples would have understood Jesus' proposal to make them "fishers of men?" What do you think Jesus meant by the term?

#	Scripture, cont.
3	What skills are involved in fishing for men? How did Jesus teach these skills to His disciples?

#	Homework due:__________
1	Help someone learn something by doing. Pick one single thing—a skill, a poem, a song, anything—and teach it to one person. Instead of just talking to them about this thing, guide them so that they learn by doing. They don't even have to know that you taught them anything!
2	**Prayerfully** read back through the Scripture passages again and ask God to apply His Word to your heart so that you may understand the fullness of your identity in Christ (Ephesians 1:17-23). Take time to listen as you pray, and ask the Lord to give you insight and clarity into who you are.

Week Two: day 2

Missionary Identity

Mission is not something we do, it's something we are. Early church fathers used the word "mission" to refer to the interaction between the persons of the Holy Trinity; the Father sends the Son, and together they send the Spirit. This most basic understanding of mission is referred to as the Missio Dei, the mission of God. In modern times, the word "mission" has been used in reference to God's purposes to extend this divine communion to humanity through Christ. From the beginning, God has revealed Himself to be a missionary God. Everything that He does is either sending or gathering for His glory.

#	Scripture
1	Read Philippians 2:5-11 a couple times. In what ways does this passage speak of Jesus as though He were a traditional missionary?
2	How is Christ's example of incarnation ("emptying Himself... taking the form of a servant") shape our understanding of God's mission?

Missionary Dysfunction

Imagine you have signed up for a mission trip. You are headed to an Asian country to help dig a well and host backyard Bible clubs. Your time is fully scheduled and mapped out. You board the plane and arrive on time, ready to hit the ground running. However, as you exit the plane and gather your luggage, you receive a phone call letting you know that the week's activities have been cancelled due to unforeseen circumstances. You now have a team on the ground in a foreign country with a week of unscheduled time ready to work for the sake of the gospel. Think about this: How do you proceed? Do you hop back on the plane and reschedule? How do you think a "missionary" would handle this situation? How would he think? How would he incarnate the gospel in the time he had? What tools would he need?

Unfortunately, most Christians in this situation would be clueless about how to proceed. They've not been trained to think far beyond sanctification in their discipleship process. Most would be utterly dependant on a traditional missionary to assign them tasks, which they would joyfully complete. But in doing so, they are really not living out their own identities as missionaries. They are merely serving as teachers or construction workers, which are noble activities. They would be living out their identities, though, if they were missionary teachers and missionary construction workers, employing the skills that belong to those who bear a missionary identity.

Throughout history, God not only speaks to people, He sends them. He gives them purpose, and that purpose shapes their identity. "Go," He says, "and be an agent of salvation." He actually uses sending language, "I am sending you... ." Noah, Abraham, and Moses are examples. Christ, of course, is the ultimate example, having been sent into the world so that the world, through Him, might be saved (John 3:16-17). The early Church responded to the gospel, and they went. They understood their call to join Jesus on His mission, and that sentness shaped their identities. It makes no sense to talk about our faith, our Savior, or even God outside the context of mission. The Church exists to organize people on mission. Without mission, there is no Church, and we have no meaningful connection to one another.

If mission is so central to shaping our identity, we need to be sure to include it in our discipleship process. Missionaries must understand missionary skill and practice.

#	Quesions
1	How would you adjust your lifestyle if you were to consider yourself a missionary where you are? What would you do differently?
2	In what ways are you culturally a "national" (one of the people to whom you'd like to minister)? What do you have in common with others around you?

#	Questions, cont.
3	In what ways are you a "missionary" (an outsider different from the people you live among)? How does the process of becoming a disciple of Jesus affect your status as an "insider" to a given culture or context? Do you remain an insider, even in your own home culture?
4	How could the discipleship process prepare believers for an experience in which they need to think about a culture and community like a missionary?

Week Two: day 3

Tricks of the Trade

In the following chapters, we will cover nine basic missionary skills, or tradecraft, that we believe are foundational to missionary thought and activity. These skills are commonly taught to international missionaries before they set out to foreign lands. But these are not only "international missionary skills;" they are necessary for all churches to teach all believers. These skills are for all Christians everywhere and in every vocation, in the context of the local church.

Some of these skills will be immediately recognizable; others may be altogether unknown. Maybe you live in the town you grew up in, maybe you've deliberately moved to live among people who are different from you for the sake of ministry. Whether you're in professional ministry or simply living a missional life, the application of these skills is vital to your church's obedience in participating in God's global mission.

#	Activity
1	Take five minutes to brainstorm a list of skills you believe would be involved in missions. We're interested in universal missionary skills, so try to keep your list from being too specific to one particular mission field (and don't look ahead to our list of skills).

#	Scripture
1	Read Matthew 5:13-16. What are the figurative meanings of salt and light? In what ways are you as a follower of Jesus salt and light?
2	Is "being salt and light" something you naturally know how to do? If not, how do you learn to do it?

#	Homework due:__________
1	Think about your daily schedule. Outside of work and church, what activities are you involved in on a regular basis (please include those activities that involve your children as well)?
2	How can you be salt and light in those contexts?

#	Homework, cont.
3	What "skills" do you need to develop in order to be salt and light in your given context?
4	Take a few minutes to think about or read through some of the stories in the Gospels. What skills do you read about Jesus employing as He lived and preached the gospel to others?
5	**Pray** simply that you would be salt and light in your context. Pray that you and your church would equip one another in the thought and practice of those participating in God's mission.

Week Two: day 4

What Skills?

What, if anything, do you know about the missionary applications of these Tradecraft skills? After each of the following terms, write everything that comes to mind upon reading them:

#	What Skills?
1	Following the Spirit
2	Mapping
3	Cultural exegesis
4	Building relationships

#	What Skills? cont.
5	Finding the person of peace
6	Contextualization
7	Pursuing alternative paths into mission
8	Protecting indigeneity

Missionary tradecraft are the tools that make it possible for you to do what you were made to do. Practice them until they become second nature, and you will be equipped to do ministry in any context. Our hope is that by mastering these skills, your church will learn to think and act like the missionary it is meant to be.

This list of skills is by no means exhaustive. There are many, many more to be learned and employed. The skills we have chosen to expound upon in the pages to follow are basic, important, practical, and relatively unknown.

#	Questions
1	What missionary skills (in the list above or others that are not mentioned here) have you already learned? How did you learn them?
2	How have you applied those skills in your life?

#	Homework due:_________
1	Take a few minutes today to walk or bike around your neighborhood. What observations can you make about your neighborhood and its inhabitants? Who is there? When are they there? What do they do when they are there?
2	Spend a few minutes **pray**ing for some of the needs your observations may have brought to mind.

Week Two: day 5

Tricks of the Trade

As we embark on the journey of exploring missionary skills, we invite you to wrestle through the application of these skills in your own context. Whether you're serving in East Asia or West Virginia, we believe that these skills will radically affect how you obediently engage the people around you with the gospel of Jesus Christ.

Much of what you will study here is usually reserved for the professionals, held aside for those who are full-time Christian workers in foreign contexts. As we pull back the curtain on these skills in the following chapters, pay particular attention to the commonalities between international mission and mission in your local context.

Think not only about how you can apply these skills individually, but also how your church might make them a regular part of discipleship and employ them in local ministry as well as international.

#	Question
1	We have been challenged over the years to take the gospel to the nations. Certainly, we should take the gospel to the nations, but in what ways have the nations come to us? How can we see the nations in our own particular contexts and communities?

#	Homework due:__________
1	Search the internet to find the nations that are represented in your city's school system, particular professions, and neighborhoods. As fully as you can, list the nations represented in your city. If you can, try to identify areas of your city where certain people groups may be found.
2	What ministries does your church currently have that focus on people from other cultures? How are the people involved in these ministries being trained to interact with people from other cultures?

#	Homework, cont.
3	Look around at the various businesses, restaurants, and even neighborhoods. Do you have any in your area that are geared for internationals? List them here. How are they different from others in the area?
4	Are there any places of worship in your area that are not Christian? If so, please list them. How do they differ from one another and Christian places of worship? Is there a culture created around and from those spaces?
5	**Pray** now for the internationals you have identified in your city. Pray for yourself and your church, that you would be aware and well-trained in order to cross cultures with the gospel. As you pray, listen and brainstorm ways that you might approach internationals in your city and incarnate the gospel in ways that they see and understand despite cultural boundaries.

Week Two: Questions for Group Discussion

#	Questions
1	What skills does a good missionary need to develop? What is good missionary tradecraft?
2	How many of these skills are you already familiar with? Where did you learn them? How many of these skills do you see currently being taught and employed within your church? Where are they being taught?
3	Where do we find the idea of "sentness" in Scripture? Give specific examples. How does sentness shape identity? Whose identity does it shape?

#	Questions, cont.
4	Discuss the example from Day 2 involving the mission trip with the schedule that fell apart. How would you handle such a situation?
5	Discuss several examples of people in Scripture whose identity was shaped by their sentness. How did they change after being sent by God?

#	Questions, cont.
6	You spent time on Day 5 thinking about and praying for internationals in your city. How would ministry among internationals differ from ministry to others in your city? Does missionary tradecraft apply in either situation?

Take time to affirm one another in your missionary identity. Think of ways to encourage one another (go to Scripture together) to walk according to your call, as who you were made to be. Talk about your individual situations and contexts. Point out skills that may be particularly pertinent to others in the group as they join God on mission. Pray together for strength, creativity, and sensitivity as you learn about your identity and your city for His purposes there.

Week Three: day 1

Following the Spirit

#	Activity
	Imagine yourself as a leader in a newly planted church. You have a small core group, some of whom have been expressing interest in global mission. Now you and the rest of your leadership are faced with many questions: Where will we go? Who will go? How will we pay? What will we do once we are there? These questions don't even begin to scratch the surface of the deep and difficult questions you will face.
1	How do you go about answering the questions? Let's narrow the scope a bit. How do you answer the first question—where/to whom are you sent? Are there practical steps to be taken?
2	Now, imagine yourself a leader in a large established church with no real direction for mission, just a lot of random, disconnected short-term trips. You need to find some direction. Answer the same question as above. How do you decipher where/to whom you are sent?

The First Question

Interestingly, even though the two churches above are very different and find themselves in different situations, they are really asking the same question, "To whom and to where are we sent?" It is an important question. Everything that a church does in mission hinges on how they answer that particular question.

There have been many methodologies developed for determining the answers to these questions over the years of missionary activity. Most of them offer a particular answer to your question, not a way to answer the question yourself. They remove you from the actual decision-making process, and that is an important distinction to recognize. Strategies are fine, but one-size-fits-all versions can be dangerous solutions and deprive the local church of some of the spiritual work and skill-building involved in deriving strategy.

You may have heard of some of the common strategies churches have adopted over the years:

- **Focus on the 10/40 window**
- **Focus on the least reached peoples (UPGs and UUPGs)**
- **Focus on large urban centers where there are less than 2 percent of the people evangelized but over 100,000 in population**
- **Invest in local church planters or pastors**
- **Invest in near culture church planters or pastors**

All of these approaches have the intent to fulfill the Great Commission and can be useful tools for the church on mission. While we can learn from effective strategies, we must determine the source of our direction in mission. There are so many varying strategies that a church would be taking a shot in the dark to choose between them. The tools are just not enough; they do not stand on their own.

#	Homework due:__________
1	Think about the missions emphasis in your own church. Has your church adopted any of these strategies? If so, what led to determining the church's approach?
2	How was the vision for the people/place you focused on communicated to the congregation? Do the people share a common vision and heart for the people among whom you are working?
3	**Pray** for God's continued direction in your life and your local church as it pertains to whom He has sent you. Pray for boldness to follow as the Spirit leads you.

Week Three: day 2

How Do We Know?

> My own experience as a missionary has been that the significant advances of the church have not been the result of our own decisions about mobilizing and allocating of 'resources.' The significant advances in my experience have come through happenings of which the story of Peter and Cornelius is a paradigm, in ways of which we have no advance knowledge. God opens the heart of a man or woman in the gospel.[1]

Even when offered a list of engagement strategies, the church still faces questions—How do we decide where to engage? Which strategy is right for us? Is there a program we should adopt? Which statistics are right?

More importantly, there are more basic questions churches should be asking. What does Scripture have to say on how we develop our mission strategy? How do we balance our plans and the Spirit's guidance?

#	Scripture
	Read the story of Peter and Cornelius in Acts 10, and answer the following questions:
1	What was Peter's strategy? To whom was he taking the good news of Jesus?

1 Lesslie Newbigin, *The Open Secret*, 1995, 64.

#	Scripture, cont.
2	What changed Peter's heart? What might have happened had he continued in his pre-planned strategy?

Jesus Gave Us a Gift

Jesus received the authority for His mission from God the Father (Matthew 28:18-20). Jesus only did the things He saw and heard from the Father (John 5:19), and He was led by the Spirit (Matthew 4:1). Jesus passed the responsibility and authority for mission on to His followers. His expectation was that they would be led in the same way He was. The agent—the direction and strength for sending—is the Spirit. Jesus said to them again, "Peace be with you. As the Father has sent me, even so I am sending you." And when he had said this, he breathed on them and said to them, "Receive the Holy Spirit" (John 20:21-22).

The initial objective of Jesus' plan was to enlist men who could bear witness to His life and carry on His work after He returned to the Father.[2]

In other words, our missionary endeavors are not on our own. The mission is God's, and He has not sent us into that mission alone. That was Jesus' promise in Matthew 28:20, which He reiterated with a twist just before His ascension:

> But you will receive power when the Holy Spirit has come upon you, and you will be my witnesses in Jerusalem and in all Judea and Samaria, and to the end of the earth (Acts 1:8).

The power to "be witnesses" came from the indwelling Spirit. God was with them as He sent them out on mission giving them authority, direction, and strength for the missionary life ahead.

#	**Homework** due:__________
1	What other examples can you find in Scripture where Jesus was following the direction of the Spirit?

2 Robert Coleman, *The Master plan of Evangelism*, 1993, 21-22.

#	Homework, cont.
2	Thinking about your own life and that of your local church, name specific times when you (and/or your church) have followed the leadership of the Spirit in a way that was different than you expected.
3	**Pray** for God's continued direction in your life and your local church as it pertains to whom He has sent you. Pray for boldness to follow as the Spirit leads you.

Week Three: day 3

It's Spiritual

Common sense is a part of discerning your church's missionary call. The gifts of the people that comprise your local body should impact deeply the direction you move in mission. But there is also a spiritual aspect—something supernatural and beyond our control. That is, the work of the Holy Spirit. We must not forget, our missional endeavors are not on our own, they are God's. As such, God guides us by His Spirit.

#	Questions
1	What is the role of the Holy Spirit in the life of the believer? (list as fully as you can with Scripture references. Hint: John 16:7-8; 14:26; Romans 8:14; Galatians 5:18, 25, et al.)

#	Questions, cont.
2	In accordance with the list you just made, how does the Spirit's role relate to our ability to effectively join God on mission?

The Leadership Void

Imagine the fear, wonder, excitement, doubt, questions, and awe that must have flooded the minds of Jesus' followers as they watched Him ascend into the clouds. He had been killed for the mission that He had just assigned to them. And He had stayed among the Jews. He wanted them to go to all the nations with the good news of God's kingdom. But how? Who would lead them? Who would show them where and how to go? Jesus had been their leader. They went where He sent them and did what He said to do. But now He was gone. But He had not left them alone (John 14:25-31).

After a time of waiting (a week or so), the leadership void was filled—powerfully! The Holy Spirit came to indwell Jesus' followers and empower them as witnesses to all the earth (Acts 1:8; 2:1-12). In short, it was the Holy Spirit who came to lead Jesus' followers on the mission He had entrusted to them; and the Holy Spirit remains our leader as we join God on mission today (Galatians 5:25).

> …our necessary dependence on the step-by-step leadership of the Holy Spirit is often an afterthought in mission. We tend to consult Him once, then ask for His blessing on our strategy rather than allow Him to guide our every turn along the way. Our mission depends on the Holy Spirit's guidance every step of the way.
>
> —Caleb Crider, co-founder of The Upstream Collective

"There is no question that God's people can look for and expect 'leadings,' 'guidance,' 'indications' of what they are meant to do."[3]

Our tendency as individuals and as local churches and mission agencies is to subscribe, sometimes blindly, to a prescribed strategy without a constant listening and discerning ear tuned into the heartbeat of our Lord.

#	Questions
1	Can you describe a time in your life when you discerned a specific call from God to a certain activity, but then you devised a strategy of your own accord?

3 Martyn Lloyd-Jones, *The Sovereign Spirit,* 1986, 89-90.

#	Questions, cont.
2	What about in your local church, with a small group, or a certain ministry?

#	Activity
1	Set aside for a moment the leadership of the Spirit. Imagine your local church felt a call to a certain people. What steps would you naturally take to begin to develop strategy (i.e. Internet searches, partnerships with agencies, meeting locals, vision trips, etc.)?

#	Activity, cont.
2	How might it look to now think through that list under the direction of the Spirit? How might He change your strategy? Are there other ways He might connect you with the people He is sending you to that are not on your list?

#	Homework due:__________
1	All of this "Spirit-led" talk leads us to the question of strategy-driven approaches: What happens when God wants us to do something or go somewhere outside the norm of our philosophical or anthropological strategies (e.g., Peter in Acts 10)? What happens when God says, "no?"
2	Think about times in God's story in which He told people "no." In what times did God "shame the wisdom of the wise" by sending people to unexpected places and in unexpected ways? Describe a few here:

#	Homework, cont.
3	God often does use the weak to shame the wise (1 Corinthians 1:27) throughout Scripture. Why do we think He would change that now (this is not hypothetical—please answer this question)?
4	It seems that the main reason we hope God will work differently in our situations is control rooted in pride. God's strength is perfected in our weakness (2 Corinthians 12:9), which means that our part is to be weak and vulnerable, moldable, and lead-able. It requires humility, such as was required of Christ to take on human form and endure the cross (Philippians 2:5-8). Straight up, it's hard, and it requires constant communion with and deference to our King. **Pray** that the mind of Christ that is already in you would lead you to humbly follow the leadership of the Spirit, not just once, but continually—step-by-step. Pray that the Spirit would lead your church, and that together you would boldly follow as God leads you on mission, even in unexpected ways.

Week Three: day 4

There Is a Pattern

One might read this study and believe that its authors are anti-strategy. That would be unfortunate, because it is untrue. Strategy is necessary for effective engagement. Randomly picking a strategy from a website or some other list and sticking to it "come what may" is the problem.

There is a pattern to be gleaned from the Bible. The problem is that it is a rather fluid pattern, driven by relationship. Just about everyone we read of in the early church that acted as "missionaries" had some sort of developed personal mission strategy. The caveat was that each of those missionaries was willing to stray from that strategy when led by the Spirit to do so.

We read on Day 3 about Peter in Acts 10, whose focus was the Jews. Following the leadership of the Spirit (10:19-20), he diverged from that path and went to Cornelius' house, a Gentile, and the entire household was saved. Paul wrote to the Romans (15:20) that his strategy was to preach where no one else had—where the name of Christ was not known, which he practiced. However, he obediently strayed from his pragmatism when the Spirit led (see Acts 16).

Selah

You do not necessarily need to write answers to these questions, but spend time meditating on them honestly. Journal anything the Lord brings to mind for your own edification and growth:

> If the Spirit were to forbid us from doing something as essential to our mission as preaching the Word to a given people (as happened with Paul in Acts 16), would we do it? Would you do it?
>
> If He prevented you from meeting some obvious need, would you recognize it as Him?
>
> Are you willing to accept "no" as an answer from the Lord? What is difficult about "no" as an answer from the Lord?
>
> How would you know if He was saying "no" to you?
>
> Try to recall a time that the Lord thwarted your efforts somehow; changed your plans from the pre-determined strategy. Can you remember such a time? If not, why do you think that is? Have you always followed the correct

strategy or have you been so focused on the strategy that you missed the voice of the Lord redirecting you?

Listen and Obey

Sounds simple enough, right? Listen and obey—that is the pattern that Scripture demonstrates and prescribes. Be in close enough relationship with Jesus that you "hear and know His voice" and follow Him (John 10:27). It is by the Spirit we were called into life and relationship in Christ; therefore, we should also walk, step-by-step with the Holy Spirit (Galatians 5:25).

In the Scriptures, we find story after story in which an individual receives direction, calling, or prompting by the Holy Spirit and follows it with faithful obedience. The listening does not end there, as in many of those stories, the Spirit continues to lead later on, and the recipient is faced with continual choices between obedience and disobedience.

Within our churches, we find ourselves in the same position, trying to discern God's direction in mission. Speaking of the root causes of great historical advances of the church in mission, Leslie Newbigin wrote, "It was not part of any missionary strategy devised by the church. It was the free and sovereign deed of God, who goes before His church. And, like Peter, the church can usually find good reasons for being unwilling to follow. But follow it must if it is to be faithful. For the mission is not ours, but God's."[4]

4 Newbigin, *The Open Secret*, 64.

#	**Homework** due:_________
1	How would you handle a situation in which you believe the Lord is leading you somewhere that defies conventional wisdom/logic (i.e. you are called to go somewhere outside of the strategic "norm")? How do you handle situations in which the discerned direction just doesn't make sense (think Jonah, Peter in Acts 10, Paul in Acts 16, etc.)? How would it be handled within your church?
2	Take time to read the entirety of John 10 prayerfully. **Pray** that you would know Jesus' voice, and boldly obey Him. Pray that your church would do the same as you engage your neighborhoods and the nations with the good news of Jesus.

Week Three: day 5

Pragmatism Breeds Models

If you want to know how to do just about anything, there is a model for it. Someone has done it before, and they'll sell you a book or some mp3s or DVDs so you can learn for just three easy payments. And we buy them all. At some level, we are all pragmatists; we tend to value, and therefore mimic, what works. It is true in almost every facet of life, including the Church and mission. And if a given model works, then God must be blessing it; and it must be the "right way" to do it.

A stroll through the local Christian book store reveals our pragmatic bent. The successful pastor/missionary/Christian entrepreneur/youth worker/church planter writes a book detailing exactly how he achieved success in his field. It becomes an instant best-seller, because everyone hoping to be successful in the same field immediately buys the book and implements the steps. And a model is born.

Pragmatism in mission has produced models, as well. Only go where there is an obvious harvest; only go where results come quickly; only go to a people group we define as "least-reached." The list could go on. The question is, "If something draws a crowd who might listen to us, is it always good? Is it the best thing?" What if God leads us to do something that does not quickly, or ever, produce visible results?

A tension exists here between "what works" and "what we are called to." They may not necessarily be the same thing. The fact that something "worked" for someone else does not make it the de facto model for everyone else in mission. We must fight our tendency toward pragmatism. In the beginning, we must forget strategies. The Holy Spirit is our only guide for mission.

#	Activity
1	Compile a list of every strategy for mission you can think of. List every felt need and every reason for going on mission you have heard (use another piece of paper if needed):

#	Activity, cont.
2	Overwhelmed yet? How do you discern which of these needs or strategies is right for you and your church (if any of them is)?
3	Give examples of pragmatic practice within the church (following after "what works"). Can you see examples in your own life and in your local church?

Characteristics of Spirit-led Churches

Up until a certain point in God's story, people were called in most cases on an individual basis; think Abram, Moses, Joshua, Isaiah, the disciples, etc. (though, of course the Israelites were called and led as a people, as well). In Acts 13, however, we find a prescriptive shift, as Paul and Barnabas are called by the Spirit and sent in the context of community. Believers were gathered, unified by the Spirit, and He guided them to the specifics of missionary engagement.

The church is God's vehicle to carry out mission in the world, so it makes sense that He would call and send by His Spirit through the local church. There are three characteristics we have seen that are shared by churches who are Spirit-led in their mission effort:

1. The church has a close communion with God. Obvious as it seems, it pervades their culture. They regularly pray, fast, study, listen, and learn together. They practice obedience together and do not succumb to pragmatic tendencies.
2. The church understands its call to the nations. Mission is not just a program within these churches; instead, it defines them. Everything the church does keeps in mind its missionary purpose.
3. The church is highly motivated and committed to seeing missions implemented in the life of their church, both globally and locally. They model mission in their city and around the world, and they develop the vision into a workable strategy for the church.

If the church is listening together, practicing obedience, and developing the missionary identity of its people, the Spirit will lead the church as it lives out the Great Commission in their community and abroad. Once a church zeros in on where the Spirit is leading them to be involved, the right opportunities will begin to emerge.

#	Homework due:__________
1	Think honestly and critically about your life. Where has pragmatism crept in (i.e. Bible study, prayer, local ministry, etc.)? How can you re-think pragmatic decisions and make adjustments in how you relate to God and others?

#	Homework, cont.
1	
2	Now complete the above exercise as it pertains to your church. Where have you as a body fallen into pragmatism, finding what works and duplicating it? Has it "worked" for you? Either way, is it the best thing for your church? Your community? How can you, without causing division but keeping the unity of the body (Ephesians 4:3), begin to work to move beyond pragmatism and implement a more Spirit-led approach?
3	Read the account of Paul and Barnabas' sending in Acts 13 and meditate on how their sending took place. Think about what the church was doing, how unified they must have been, and how quick they were to obey. **Pray** for the same attitudes and actions within your own church. Pray again that the Spirit would lead your church together to the people/place He is sending you as a unified body. Pray that you would be sensitive and discerning all along the way.

Week Three: Questions for Group Discussion

#	Questions
1	What is the "first question" in mission? Why is it an important one? How is it most often answered?
2	Discuss your answers to the questions from Day 2 regarding Peter and Cornelius in Acts 10.
3	Where did Jesus receive the authority to carry out His mission? Where do we receive the authority to continue carrying out that mission? Where is this found in Scripture? What does this authority mean about how we carry out the mission?

#	Questions, cont.
4	When devising a strategy for mission activity, what are the common sense/pragmatic decisions? What parts are more spiritual? How do you differentiate between the two?
5	Discuss times in your lives/church when you have sensed the clear leading of the Spirit to engage in something. How did you hear? How did you respond?
6	Discuss times when God has told you "no." How did you respond? What about when He changed your plans?

#	Questions, cont.
7	Discuss the Newbigin quote from Day 4 regarding historical advances of the church, "It was not part of any missionary strategy devised by the church. It was the free and sovereign deed of God, who goes before His church. And, like Peter, the church can usually find good reasons for being unwilling to follow. But follow it must if it is to be faithful. For the mission is not ours, but God's." Is he correct? Can/does the church justify not doing the things God wants us to with good reason?

#	Questions, cont.
8	Discuss the characteristics of a Spirit-led church. Are you able to see those things within your local church? What else could/should be added to the list? Are there other characteristics common to Spirit-led churches?

Spend some time talking through and praying about the different approaches to sending people into mission. Talk honestly. Remember Scripture and read it. Pray that God would show you how your local body should endeavor to be on mission together. Pray for His grace, that you would walk in unity together as you discover His direction for your church.

"... be filled with the Spirit, addressing one another in psalms and hymns and spiritual songs, singing and making melody to the Lord with all your heart, giving thanks always and for everything to God the Father in the name of our Lord Jesus Christ, submitting to one another out of reverence for Christ." Ephesians 5:18b-21

Week Four: day 1

Mapping

I'm Lost!

Nothing will accent the fact that you are an outsider in a certain place more than being lost there. This is particularly true if you are in a completely foreign culture and do not speak the local language. Nothing screams, "I don't belong!" quite like looking for someone who speaks your language so they can give you directions to wherever you are trying to go. You can learn much from an experience of this nature, but it can be an incredibly frustrating, and even frightening experience.

Being lost is stressful, at best. When we are lost, we look for anything that might help us be, well, un-lost. Signs help, if you can read the language. Asking for directions works, as long you can decipher the local perspective (turn left by Jimmy's broken-down pickup truck). The best solution for lostness, apart from a personal guide, is a good map. It can show you where you are, where you want to go, and the paths between the two.

Story Time

Recount a time you have been lost (don't act like you haven't been). Where were you? What were you doing? How did you realize you were lost? What did you do? How did you feel? Were you ever in danger? How did you remedy the situation? How could you have avoided being lost in the first place?

Mapping is an invaluable skill useful for avoiding just that sort of lostness in mission. After following the Spirit's direction to a people and place, one of the best ways to get a "lay of the land" is through mapping—compiling a multi-layer graphical representation of the area to which you have been sent. An outsider wanting to begin ministry in a new place can gain valuable insight from simply walking the streets and documenting everything observed. Studying the city can give you great strides in understanding its people; and putting yourself in the shoes of the people to whom you want to minister is the first step of incarnation.

It's Just Useful ...

Good map-making is the fieldwork out of which strategy is formed. It is the intelligence-gathering portion of developing your approach to ministry. Knowing who and where the people are is key to your ability to work among them. Maps serve as a tool to help you organize your initial observations (and developments over time) and coordinate with others to develop an understanding of how people think, live, and interact. It also serves as an introductory project to introduce you to the community. It is something to do before you know "what to do." While you are walking the neighborhood, you will also have the opportunity to meet people, initiate conversation, become conversant in local culture, and pray for the people there.

The Basics ...

Missionary maps do not have to be complicated. It doesn't have to be drawn from scratch. Depending on where you are going, there is likely an online or printed map already in existence. Pick one that suits you, or, if you so desire, draw your own in a notebook or Photoshop or plot one out on Google Maps. Just be aware that your map will be a working document that will change over time as you gain insight about your community and people.

One of the best things about a good map is that it is an easy way to pass on what you have learned about a city or neighborhood to a partner with whom you'd like to work. Imagine sharing all that you know of a city with a new worker who has joined you in your city; or using your map to train a team from your sending church who will be joining you for a short term trip. The information on your map is invaluable, and with the groundwork already laid, others will have a much easier time getting a grasp of your city as they prepare to minister there.

#	Activity
1	**Activity** The following page has a defined space for you to draw a map. Quickly, without too much thought or effort, draw a sketch of your city (the city as a whole, not just your neighborhood) as if someone who is not familiar with your community was asking for a quick "fly-over." What would be important to include and why?
2	As you work through this exercise, **pray** for your city. Ask God to give you some new insight into the city and its people. Look for something, even in your own drawing, that you've never really paid attention to before. Pray, as well, for the churches in your city. Pray that they would faithfully join God on mission in your city and around the world.

Mental Map Exercise 1: Quickly sketch a map as if for someone who is not familiar with the community. Include significant features in the area and label them. (5 minutes)

Week Four: day 2

There Is More to It.

Ministry requires more than knowing the names and locations of streets and highways in your city. Observations need to be made in multiple dimensions. Ideally, your map would have at least three layers: **geographic** (physical layout of the city), **social** (where people live work, shop, and play, how they behave and why), and **spiritual** (where/what people worship, revere, and fear).

Geography: Mapping the Space

The first step in developing a map is to plot physical locations in and around a city. In the 1960s, American urban planner Kevin A. Lynch conducted an extensive study[5] of how urban dwellers navigate their environments and outlined what he identified as the five "elements" of the city. These were the most basic building blocks of a person's understanding of the urban environment and have been used to great effect by missionaries and local church planters to help them understand the cities in which they find themselves. The following is a brief look at those elements:

PATHS NODES DISTRICTS EDGES LANDMARKS

PATHS

> *The familiar routes people follow. Paths are the channels along which people customarily, occasionally, or potentially move: streets, walkways, transit lines, canals, railroads, etc.*

Paths are usually delineated with lines on a map—thick for major thoroughfares, thin or dashed for minor routes. Urban paths may include pedestrian walkways, alleys, bus routes, or subway and metro lines. Many modern cities were built along rivers and railways, which are also paths.

Paths are important because they limit an individual's experience of the city and shape his perspective of it. If you want to relate to someone, follow his paths. For example, someone who gets around by subway may not be familiar with what's above him on his underground journey. Consequently, he only knows the areas of town at either end of his commute; these are the areas that shape his understanding of the city and influence him the most.

---

5 Kevin Lynch, *The Image of the City* (Cambridge: The M.I.T. Press, 1960).

It is also important to consider the mode of transportation along a particular path. The same streets navigated by private car will provide a very different experience than for those traveling by bicycle. Mode of transportation will likewise affect one's perception of distance along a path. A bus that stops every two blocks can make a street seem much longer than it actually is simply because it takes so long to traverse. For urban dwellers, distance is a relative concept.

Exploring different paths can help you become familiar with a city. Even if you minister in a city you're extremely familiar with—the town in which you grew up—traveling along less-familiar paths will open your eyes to the experiences and perspectives of your neighbors. This exploration is where mapping begins.

NODES

> *The places where multiple paths intersect. These may be primary junctions, places of a break in transportation, a crossing or convergence of paths, moments of shift from one structure to another. A node is a distinct hub of activity: marketplaces, plazas, bus stations, or intersections.*

Nodes are centers of activity, such as plazas, squares, metro stations, parks, business centers, or shopping malls. These places, according to Lynch, are "strategic spots in a city into which an observer can enter" and allow for interaction.[6] Nodes are found at intersections, which are anywhere paths converge.

When paths cross, different sorts of people intermingle. At any given time of day, the wealthy and poor alike may be found standing together on a subway platform or street corner—something that is much less likely to happen at other points along a path. Nodes are important for gaining cultural insight because they provide the opportunity to see how these different people interact (or avoid interaction) with one another. Nodes are the best vantage points for people-watching.

Billboards, signs, and newsstands are usually found in nodes. Because nodes tend to be busy places, they are prime real estate for the dissemination of information. Organizations distribute fliers and vendors advertise here for maximum visibility. Gossip, news, and social updates happen in and around nodes. Of course, social networking has had a great impact on the spread of information by essentially becoming an additional system of virtual nodes.

As people move into nodes, their behavior may change. Rather than traveling along a path and its predictable patterns for traffic flow and behavioral norms, the observer is thrown into

---

6 Ibid., 72.

a chaotic intermingling of multiple paths and the people using them. Consequently, people often enter a node with their guard up and their bags clutched tightly. Nodes may be a great place to disseminate information, but all the noise likely means they are not the best place to try to engage someone in meaningful conversation.

DISTRICTS

> *Areas with "perceived internal sameness."[7] Districts are medium-to-large sections of the city, which are recognizable as having some common identifying character: neighborhoods, suburbs, housing projects.*

This may be a neighborhood or group of neighborhoods that have a distinct character. Districts may be known for their past or present function (a "garment district," "stockyards"), their settlers or inhabitants (Chinatown, Little Italy), the historical reputation and social stigma (Skid Row, Hell's Kitchen, Red Light), architecture (historic, warehouse, tract housing additions), or geographic location (downtown, uptown, docks, waterfront, etc.).

Most urban dwellers develop a sense of identity around the districts in which they live, play, or do business. Each district has a reputation within the city and brings the expectation that a certain "type" of person might be found there.

Districts play a key part in the development of a city's personality and are determining factors in social segmentation. The district in which a person lives shapes a city dweller's understanding of himself in relation to other members of society. This is evident in so-called "blue-collar" or "working-class" neighborhoods where social and economic forces can make it hard for someone to move away.

Every population segment has its own sub-culture, language, and rules that present barriers and bridges to the spread of the gospel. When it comes to mission in the city, urban segmentation may be seen as analogous to the anthropological concept of "people groups," as outlined by missiologist Ralph Winter.[8] From this perspective, the missionary may need to take a different approach to gospel ministry for each district in the city.

EDGES

> *Dividing lines between districts. They are the linear elements not used or considered as paths by the observer. The termination of a district is an edge: shores, railroad cuts, edges of development, walls.*

7 Lynch, 66

8 Ralph Winter, "Unreached Peoples and Beyond (1974 to Now)," YouTube, last modified September 2015, http://youtube.com/watch?v=S8KBHqjld5k.

Edges are the boundaries of a district. According to Lynch,[9] the linear elements not used or considered as paths by the observer are where one district ends and another may begin. Edges are the borders between two places, linear breaks in the continuity of the space. Common edges are things like shores, edges of a housing development, walls, highways, rivers, etc.

As a city grows, the construction of a new interstate or commercial zone might divide an older neighborhood, effectively making one district into two. In a district with heavy foot traffic, anything that is difficult to cross often forms an edge. Leaving one district and entering another may be as simple as crossing a street. In other instances, tunnels, bridges, gates, and crossings allow people to move between districts. Other "edges" may be less obvious; we may not be able to pinpoint exactly where one district ends and another begins, but we know when we've moved from one to another.

People tend to stay in their districts, the places in which they are most comfortable, crossing edges when they must (think of the "other side of the tracks," in which, literally, the railroad tracks are an edge). The missionary must pay particular attention to the edges. All too often, the missionary thinks in terms of physical proximity and access while ignoring the social boundaries that have been set up all around the city.

Crossing boundaries isn't the job of the audience; it's the job of the missionary. Of course, as people come to faith and are discipled toward maturity, they should be challenged to move beyond the edges, to deliberately leave one district in order to live out the gospel in another. Inviting people to cross an edge in order to hear the gospel may get in the way of inviting them to follow Jesus.

LANDMARKS

Points of reference defined by physical objects with prominent visual features, usually large and visible: a building, sign, store, park, or mountain.

The word "landmarks" brings to mind towers and monuments, but when mapping, anything that stands out as noticeable can serve as a landmark. Lynch found that people use such objects, structures, and places to navigate the city.[10] In giving directions to outsiders, residents use easily recognized landmarks: "Turn right at the drug store." For insiders, they may use something more familiar, like "turn at Kevin's house."

Landmarks can be architectural details, such as distinctive gas-lit street lamps, cobblestone streets, or white picket fences—

9 Lynch, 62.

10 Lynch, 78.

anything that helps a person determine where he is. Even if the landmarks don't give away exact locations, an insider can use them to decipher what sort of place she's in. In many cities, immigrant neighborhoods are marked with satellite dishes (to get broadcasts from home) and clothes drying on clotheslines (clothes dryers can be expensive).

Landmarks usually have lasting historical and cultural significance as well. A city built along a river will be shaped by it in many ways. These landmarks have significant and lasting effects on the people who pass them every day. Symbols of rebellion, oppression, religion, and independence emblazon themselves on the hearts of the citizens of a city.

In His earthly ministry, Jesus used landmarks to His advantage. In John 4, we read that Jesus found the "Woman at the Well," at Jacob's Well in Samaria. This landmark would have been a central part of life for many Samaritans, but different types of people would have been found there at different times of the day. His "Sermon on the Mount" used that landmark to both facilitate and distinguish what would become His best-known teachings. The same would have been true of various city gates, mountains, the rivers, and so on.

In fact, God's people are instructed to be builders of landmarks. In the book of Joshua resides eight examples of God's faithful piling rocks at the sites of His special provision, protection, or victory. These monuments served as reminders to future generations of God's faithfulness. In many cases, it can be said that a city's existing monuments, though built in ignorance to God's role, might also be redeemed with memories of the Most High. The missionary can use landmarks as bridges for the communication of the gospel.

High Places

Dr. Thom Wolf, who was among the first sociologists to apply Lynch's findings to urban missions, has pointed out[11] that each layer of the map informs the others. For example, in most cultures, areas with higher physical elevations tend to be assigned some level of importance. "Sacred" structures are often built in these locations and can have significant influence upon a city's history and culture. High places, therefore, can have direct spiritual significance to a missionary's work.

Athens, like most cities in the Roman Empire, was an acropolis built on a hilltop to make it visible yet easily defended. The most important buildings—temples, palaces, castles, and government buildings—were built on the highest points. In Acts

11 Thomas A. Wolf, "The City" (lecture presented at Golden Gate Baptist Theological Seminary, San Francisco, California, January, 2000).

17, we read that the Apostle Paul went up to the Areopagus, an amphitheater-like structure built on a hilltop, where philosophers and city elders would gather to discuss current events, consider social issues, and make decisions. This "high place" had spiritual significance to the missionary and provided a tremendous opportunity for contextualized gospel proclamation.

In nearly every city in the world, the high places are significant historically, culturally, geographically, and spiritually. The very existence of high places says much about the people who built them. By observing the high places, you'll see how people in your city assign value and meaning to places. They don't treat all people and places equally. Power, importance, and influence are either ascribed, earned, or bought, and whatever the city's fathers have done in raised elevations will reveal what influences the citizens of that city. High places should be among the first things plotted on the missionary's map.

#	Homework due:__________
1	Go back to your map and add the symbols for the five elements above. Think more closely about your city. How does your view of it change with these elements in mind? Where are the "high places?" Does this change the way you view your city? Could it change the way you navigate it? How do you think your view of your own city would change if you simply traversed it along different paths than normal? What if you hung out in different nodes or districts?

#	Homework, cont.
2	As a missionary in your city, what have you just learned about it? How could this information shape the way you do ministry there?
2	**Pray** again for your city and its people. Ask God for insight into how knowing your city well can open new opportunities for ministry. Think in particular about the "high places" in your city—where and who is it that people worship? How do you know? Pray for the wisdom to use those high places as a means to understand the people and their culture more clearly, so that you may engage them with the gospel more readily.

Week Four: day 3

Where Do Things Happen?

When thinking about your city, where is it that "things" happen? Choose a particular people group in your city. Where do they live? Where do they work? Shop? Play? Are there parts of the city they might avoid? Why?

Social: Mapping the Story

After plotting the geography of the city, the missionary should begin the social layer of the map. This layer includes who lives where, what they do, what their needs are, and how they see themselves in relation to the rest of the city. The purpose of this layer of the map is to help the missionary understand the people to whom he has been sent. This information can only come through personal interaction. As one may imagine, this section of the map may contain sensitive information such as prayer requests, needs, or personal struggles. It may be strange for a friend from your neighborhood to enter your house only to find his name written on a map displayed on your wall. Please use discretion.

Demographics, information about the people who live in a place, are fairly easy to discover. For starters, there are various sources of demographic research findings, from books to newspapers to online resources. Take demographic research with a grain of salt. Some of these studies tend to be completed under social and political pressures, and their findings can sometimes be skewed. For example, a local government may have an interest in finding a higher number of people living in poverty within the city because that could mean greater funding from the state. Other problematic statistics, such as crime rates, education scores, and receipt of social services, may likewise be downplayed or exaggerated to serve an ideological agenda.

Beginning with an intentional observation on the street, the missionary can quickly get a sense of who lives where. But demographics run deeper than what can be seen on the surface. Not all outsiders look as though they don't belong. Some immigrant groups can be harder to find because they do a better job of integrating into their host cultures. Likewise, not everyone who seems out of place truly is. Demography can include such things as survey work or the use of cultural informants. Either way, an accurate map requires personal interaction.

Need may be more difficult to gauge. Not everyone will be open and honest about his needs, especially with a stranger. Common needs would include physical security, financial stability, or companionship. Believe it or not, many people who live in large cities suffer a severe sense of loneliness. Experiencing these needs is one thing but confessing them might be another. Few people are willing to confess those needs that might make them appear weak. In order for the map to accurately reflect the needs of the community, the missionary must do a bit of investigating.

Although needs are generally individual, there is great value to annotating need on a map. What may initially seem to be an isolated incident of need may, in fact, be a community-wide problem. Mapping will help to reveal societal needs at the neighborhood and district levels. This insight can be particularly helpful in the development of strategies for community service.

Narrative is the story a community believes about itself. This story (or set of stories) is perhaps the most helpful part of the missionary's map. Sometimes, narrative is not a conscious thing—someone who lives in a working-class neighborhood may use derogatory descriptions of the wealthy who live nearby but be unaware of his prejudice against them. Another may naturally refer to himself deprecatingly, a sign of low social status.

The message of Christ is for all people everywhere. Narrative mapping allows the missionary to discern exactly how the gospel is good news to a particular group of people. Those with a victim mentality would be overjoyed to know that Christ brings justice and frees the oppressed (Luke 4:18). Those who find themselves caught in the trap of materialism need to know that the things of this world will one day pass away (1 John 2:17). Idol worshipers need to know the futility of their misguided affections (Jeremiah 10:1-5).

Through direct conversations we can begin to truly know our neighbors. We can patch together a rough outline of how people see the world around them: their personal religious experience, their goals for life, and their dreams for the future. Ultimately, this is how we can know the best way to communicate the fact that only Jesus can supply what people everywhere are looking for.

As with need, narrative may at first seem to be unrelated to geography. But mapping narrative can bring into focus neighborhood histories that are highly influential for the neighbors who live there. Adding this dimension to your map can help you see how local events can have lasting effects on the people who live in a particular area, regardless of whether those people were actually present when those events occurred.

#	Homework[12] due:__________
	Recall the people group you were thinking about earlier? Imagine that people group as "them" in an "us/them" scenario. You and your "people group" are the "us." Answer the following questions:
1	a. Who are "we" (your people)? Who are "they" (others/outsiders)? b. How do your people perceive themselves as compared to others? (We are honest/They are liars, thieves, crooked…). c. What kind of jokes or proverbs do "we" have about "them?"

12 The "Key Questions" have been adapted from Thom Wolf's ProCORE module.

#	Homework, cont.
1	d. Where do "they" live, and why? e. What separates "us" from "them?" f. What social barriers exist between the two groups—do they fraternize, intermarry, work together…? g. What are the rules for relating to outsiders (different family, clan, town, country…)?

#	Homework, cont.
2	Now, turn the previous questions around and answer them as if you were a part of the people group you chose earlier (what "they" say about "us," etc.).
3	What implications do you see here for this particular people hearing the gospel, understanding it, responding to it, gathering, reproducing, or becoming New Testament churches? How might the information in this section affect how a group or New Testament church looks?
4	**Pray** for this people group. Ask God for insight into their culture, and that He would break down walls and barriers to you and the gospel. Pray that He would use you to be a faithful representative of His kingdom among the people.

Week Four: day 4

Spiritual: Mapping God's Activity

The final layer of the missionary's map, the spiritual layer, is the most important to the missionary's work. Long before the missionary is sent, God has been working among the people of the earth. He reveals Himself through nature, conscience, and blessing. He demonstrates His character through the presence of His people around the world. Through the Scriptures, He makes Himself known as a personal God. He is not "served by human hands, as though He needed anything," yet His gospel is spread by means of humanity.

In his 1990 book, Henry Blackaby famously wrote, "when God reveals to you where He is working, that becomes His invitation to join Him in His activity."[13] As missionaries, we begin engagement by discovering where God is at work. This isn't about voices from heaven or extra-biblical revelation; the missionary discovers God at work by prayerfully interjecting himself into the society to whom he is called.

Having a map that shows the physical layout of the city and the social narrative of its people, a missionary may now turn to marking those people, opportunities, events, and places he recognizes as being spiritually significant. Physical spaces can provide an indication of possible areas of spiritual significance. Social spaces, high places, and existing spiritual structures are often frontline areas. A community's stories can also be an indicator of God's activity. Conflict, failure, success, and art can point to spiritual movement. But ultimately, prayerful interaction with people is the best way to be led by God into what He's been doing.

#	Questions
1	Answer the following questions as it pertains to the people group you chose for Day 3's activities, to the best of your ability. a. Who or what, according to your people, is god?

13 Henry Blackaby, Experiencing God: *Knowing and Doing the Will of God, Revised.* (Nashville: Broadman and Holman, 2008) 56.

#	Questions, cont.
1	b. Who is Jesus Christ to them? c. Where are their "high places?" d. Do you know of places among them where God is already at work? Explain.
2	Apart from this particular people group, what are the other places in your city where you can see that God is at work? How do you know? Are there noticeable results? How might you/your church join in the work God is already doing?

Read Ephesians 1:15-23 and **pray** that Scripture passage for your people group. Pray that God would reveal Himself to them, that their hearts would be enlightened, and that they would have hope. Pray that spiritual barriers to the gospel would fall. Pray that you would have eyes to see them and boldness to work to overcome them. Pray that these particular people would come to the saving knowledge of Jesus Christ (1 Timothy 2:4).

Week Four: day 5

The Practical ...

Making maps can be as simple or as complicated a process as you choose to make it. The following are practical helps for your map-making journey:

Mapping the Geographic Layer

Begin with the geographic layer. A street map is a good start or a printed map from Google. Some practitioners prefer to draw the map by hand as it allows you to include the distortions caused by modes of travel, hard edges, or other features that may not be clear on a regular map. If you prefer to keep the project electronic, Google Maps is a great place to start. Just be sure that your base layer shows the entirety of your focus: a region, city, neighborhood, district, or other section of the city.

Whatever the format, your map must be accessible. You should be able to easily make additions and annotations to the map as observations are made. For this reason, you may choose to carry a companion notebook, iPad, smartphone, or some other way to jot down notes to be included in the project.

Perhaps the simplest way to mark the elements of the city is to draw directly on the map using different color markers. Pushpins and colored string can be used when making holes in the wall isn't a concern. Another possible approach is to use transparent sheets that can be removed as not to obscure other information on the map such as street names and neighborhood names.

Your map is only as good as the information it shows, so be sure it includes any locations that may be significant to society, such as centers of government, education, and commerce. Many locations in urban environments are dual- or multi-use, so be creative in how you show the changing importance of various locations. Also, some annotations on your map, such as farmers markets, festivals, and celebrations may be time-dependent. Layering labels and details can help you show these realities on the map.

Keep in mind that the purpose of this layer is to help you see the city through the eyes of locals. To this end, it may be a good idea to color-code your map to draw connections. For example, if members of a certain population segment are primarily found in three different districts and tend to frequent eight different paths, you can show that connection by indicating those with the same color.

Map out more than one way to get to any given point, and be sure to keep a key for your map. This will facilitate the sharing of all the information gathered and will help with the identification of the various elements at a glance.

Mapping the Social Layer

The next layer of the map will reflect social observations of your city. This layer will indicate who lives where and the cursory information that can be found about them. In essence, this will show stereotypes and generalizations about the people who live in each sector of the map. Mark these things by using notes, labels, and note cards.

A good way to map the narrative of a district is to include clippings from local newspapers and magazines. An article about crime, for example, in a neighborhood would be relevant. Printed statistics for local schools would be particularly helpful in painting a picture of the condition of local education. The same would be true of information about businesses and profiles of residents.

The social layer would also be the place to mark information about new friends and contacts made. The name of a helpful realtor or the office of an especially sympathetic government official would help the missionary understand the social landscape of the city. This is the place to collect addresses, phone numbers, and any other information that might help in making connections. Including photographs of new people and places is a great way to remember names.

Consider the narrative layer of the map as a composite profile. The personal stories, examples of need, and news articles all fit together like puzzle pieces depicting a collage of a community's story. Each observation may not apply to the entire city or population segment but its presence nevertheless affects the story of the whole.

Mapping the Spiritual Layer

The third layer of the map shows the spiritual realities of the city. This section of the map will include churches, temples, idols, evidence of the occult, or any other place you consider to be of significance. Think of the spiritual layer as a prayer guide. By using the spiritual information contained in this layer of the map, insightful intercession may be made by volunteers through prayer. It can even help people who have not even visited a city pray for it by outlining specific needs and opportunities.

Another great use for this spiritual layer is to record place and frequency of spiritual conversation. For example, you make weekly visits to a local farmer's market and have profound personal conversations about Christ nearly every visit. If, after each encounter, you were to mark that encounter on the map, it would quickly become clear that the market is a spiritually significant place. When it comes time to make decisions about where to send volunteers, place team members, or start a Bible study, the map would reveal the strategic importance of the farmer's market.

Finally, be sure the completed map can be easily shared with others. As God blesses any missionary team with new members, the map is a great way to quickly bring them up to speed on what cultural insight the team has been able to gather. The map should be readily shared with the sending churches and other supporters of the work. As local people come to faith, it would be particularly interesting to consult them regarding the information collected on the map to see how the observations of an outsider compare with those of an insider.

#	**Homework** due:__________
1	Map out your *immediate neighborhood*. Maybe even take a walk or bike ride or do something you normally would not. See it through different eyes and look for spiritual insights. **Pray** as you go, asking God to move among your neighbors.

Week Four: Group Activity

Plan ahead to spend more time together than you normally do for group discussion. Plan for a several hour long, half-day, or day-long "field trip" together to exercise this skill in your city. Go to a part of your city with which you are fairly well-acquainted or to a part to which you feel called to work (depending on the size of your group, you may want to break up into more than one group and go to different places or different parts of the same section of town).

Once there, spend some time walking the streets, praying, watching, listening, and observing. See if you can find the five elements of the city where you are (paths, nodes, districts, edges, and landmarks). Take notes as you go, both mentally and physically. Write some things down, record notes on your phone, and talk to one another about the things you observe.

Come back together as a group and compile your map. If you went to different parts of the city, put the maps together and build a larger map. Compare the parts of the city you visited. What is similar? What is different? Who is there? Why? If you went to the same part of the city, compare notes. Did you see the same things? Make the same observations? What is similar about the maps that would be compiled by your groups? What is different? Why do you think those differences exist in what you observed?

How might the information you compiled help you minister in your city? Have you learned anything that might change something you are already doing?

If you are unable to take the "field trip" as laid out above, you can compare the maps you made on Day 1. What are the similarities in your maps? What are the differences? Why are those differences there? Try to compile the information into one larger map. What can you learn from the compiled information that will help you engage the lost in your city with the gospel of Jesus?

As you talk through this information, spend time together in **pray**er for your city. Pray particularly for any people to whom you feel called. Pray for your church—that you would be diligent to learn about your city and its people, and that knowing its people would make you better representatives of the kingdom among them. Pray for yourselves and your families individually, as well, that you would be able to employ this very practical tool in your own neighborhoods.

Week Five: day 1

Exegeting the Culture

#	Activity
	Read the following short story: "The fish instructed Manu to build a large ship, as the flood now only months away. As the rains began, Manu tied a rope from his ship to the ghasha, which safely guided him as the waters rose. The waters grew so high that the entire earth was covered. As the waters subsided, the ghasha guided Manu to a mountaintop."[14]
1	Now write the corresponding story you know from Scripture:

14 J.F. Bierlein, *Parallel Myths* (New York: Ballentine, 1994), 125.

Rebellion

The flood story above is present in Hindu folklore that predates Christianity on the Indian subcontinent. An anthropologist will tell you that cultures around the world tell remarkably similar stories—creation myths, flood stories, and tales of brothers killing brothers. Every culture has elements of the human story, fragments, perspectives, human-sided versions of what really happened. This is no accident; it is God's provision for re-introducing Himself to those who have turned away from Him. Paul refers to this pattern in his letter to the Roman church:

Read Romans 1:19-23.

Humanity, if we may speak of it as a whole, once knew God; Adam and Eve walked with Him in the garden in perfect community with their Creator. But then sin entered the picture and has diverted mankind's worship away from the Most High. Having "exchanged the truth about God for lies," humanity "worshiped and served the created things rather than the Creator."

This is at the beginning of the story for every people in every culture—rebellion. Every culture shares a memory of the themes of the human story: We were once at peace with our Creator, but then we rebelled. Since then, we have struggled to regain fellowship with Him. This reframing of reality is universal. You can see it in any culture as you listen to its stories, study its religions, and investigate its worldview.

But God is faithful. He has not left His creation without hope. In the "fullness of time," God sent Jesus. With the incarnation of the Son, God interrupted the pagan story of one particular culture in order to reveal Himself to all mankind. He tore down the false realities they had constructed, reminding them of their true origins as His creation made for community with Him.

#	Questions
1	How can these common stories, even though we would certainly say they are misplaced, be cultural bridges to gospel interaction? How can you use them to approach people of other cultures with the gospel?

#	Questions, cont.
2	Can you name other examples of common shared stories, experiences, or histories that might serve as cultural bridges?
3	As the Author of history and the Creator of humankind, God values culture. Throughout the story of humanity, from beginning to end, God creates and preserves human diversity. What was His purpose in doing so? See Genesis 11 and Revelation 7:9-10.

Cultural Diversity

It is God who created diversity (Genesis 11) because of the pride of the people who built a tower to their own glory. In essence, God fought human rebellion with diversity. In this He demonstrated that He is glorified through the creation and existence of various cultures. Yet in the picture of worship around the throne (Revelation 7), God reveals that He desires to be worshiped by different types of people.[15] He is powerful enough to divide us and then to unite us for His glory.

Human diversity also has great value to the church. Experience across cultures allows us to see how God is worshiped by people who are different from us. The book of Revelation shows us that God is pleased with this creative diversity, and promises His presence among His people as they worship. And while God's people are those who lift up His name, it isn't only the believers among the nations of the earth that remember Him.

Observe any culture in depth, and it becomes clear that the suppressed memory of the Creator is not completely forgotten. Man is continuously confronted with revelation of God's attributes through nature.[16] Furthermore, tribes around the world all have been left with the faintest notion that God exists and that things have gone terribly wrong among us.

When you're really looking for it, you can find it woven into every aspect of culture. Music, stories, social justice, advertisements, humanistic religion—everywhere you look, threads lead back to God. The Artist has left His fingerprints on His work.

15 Revelation 7:9.

16 Romans 1:19.

#	Homework due:__________
1	Where are the hints of the suppressed memory of the Creator in your own local culture? Where can you see people hinting at the attributes of God in your city? What about another culture to which God is sending you/your church with the gospel? How can you use those instances as springboards for gospel interaction?
2	**Pray** for insight into culture, particularly to see the places where people are wrestling with those suppressed memories. Ask the Lord for wisdom to engage and connect around those points of shared memory of the Creator.

Week Five: day 2

#	Question
1	How do you begin conversations about the gospel with friends, neighbors, and co-workers who are not Christians? Do you use a tool or resource, tell stories, or ... ? How do you bridge the gap in conversation and turn it to spiritual matters?

Bridges

"For His invisible attributes, namely, His eternal power and divine nature, have been clearly *perceived*, ever since the creation of the world, in the things that have been made."[17] Just as you considered in yesterday's homework, these invisible attributes have great potential for our missionary efforts. Like every good story with a twist in its plot, it all makes sense in hindsight. God's purposes, His presence, His faithful provision are much easier to see in light of salvation. Rather than having to introduce a foreign truth, missionaries take the opportunity to retell a people's stories back to them from the Kingdom perspective.

---

17 Romans 1:20

In the Scriptures, cultural exegesis is referred to as "perception."[18] The word, translated from the ancient Greek word "to understand," meant "insight based on observation."

Paul employed this very technique when he "perceived" that the citizens of Athens were devoutly religious (Acts 17:22-33). He observed shrines, monuments, and temples to various gods, recognizing that even the Greek pantheon of god myths left people longing for more. Their vague memory of humanity's connection to the Creator had led them to develop a dramatic mythology of gods behind everything they couldn't explain. Just to be sure they hadn't missed a god, they had erected at least one monument in honor of "the unknown god."

Paul took advantage of this bridge into the culture. Rather than begin the conversation by confronting their blatant idolatry, Paul told the Athenians that he knew this God they were afraid of overlooking. The Greek worldview had room for an unknown god. Paul knew the God these people had "forgotten." He proclaimed the gospel by telling the men of Athens their own story back to them in light of the gospel.

Name a time you have been able to use (or have seen) this sort of bridge into culture for gospel conversation.
Describe what happened:

Barriers

Just as cultures have bridges that facilitate the spread of the gospel, they also have barriers to it. The rituals and superstitions that people revere in place of God often keep them from understanding Him. Recognizing these barriers can likewise inform our missionary strategies. Successful communication of the gospel requires that we navigate meanings, misperceptions, and deeply held ideologies.

A friend recently found himself in a deep spiritual conversation with a neighbor. The neighbor is spiritually agnostic and doesn't believe that humans can know God, or even whether He exists. He remembers going to church a few times as a child, but he otherwise has no religious background. They spoke

---

18 Ancient Greek, γινωσκω (ginosko). Donald E. Gowan, *The Westminster Theological Wordbook of the Bible* (Westminster: John Knox Press, 2003), 280.

about the role of religion in society, and my friend tried to move the conversation from ritual and tradition to a personal relationship with Christ. You can imagine his surprise when the neighbor declared, "We Christians are responsible for committing many atrocities in the name of God."

"We? Christians? I thought you weren't religious," my friend said, "maybe I misunderstood you?"

"Oh, I'm not," his neighbor explained, "but I'm more Christian than Muslim."

To his neighbor, Christian wasn't a spiritual state or even a category of belief. It was a cultural label synonymous with western, enlightenment, American, and rational. He certainly understood there was a difference between my version of Christianity and his, but from his perspective my friend was the one co-opting the term from common American culture. According to him, we're all Christians. In the United States, a major barrier to the spread of the gospel is the predominance of cultural Christianity. It's difficult to declare the good news to people who greatly misunderstand it.

Describe a time when you have tried to overcome (or have seen) a barrier to the gospel. How did you approach it?

Cultures other than ours in America have different barriers to the spread of gospel. Societal prejudices, traditions, and ethnic tensions often prevent broad sowing of the good news. Some cultures lack even a basic spiritual vocabulary that allows for the meaningful communication of abstract concepts like God and Spirit. Imagine trying to teach someone about prayer, worship, heaven, or sin when they don't have words for any of those things!

Despite the barriers a culture may present, we are called to communicate the transforming message of salvation in Christ alone. This requires we study culture in search of bridges that facilitate the spread of the gospel and the barriers that need to be overcome in order for disciples to be made. We refer to this process of intentional, hands-on research as cultural exegesis.

#	Homework due:__________
1	Name a few more places in Scripture where we see particular cultural bridges into spiritual conversation (hint: think about Jesus in the Gospels). Describe those experiences here:
2	In the same way, describe a few Scriptural examples of barriers to the gospel to be overcome (hint: think about Jesus, as well as the epistles, which are full of cultural barriers the early Christians were facing):

#	Homework, cont.
3	As you recount those stories from Scripture, **pray**erfully consider again your own surroundings. Where are the bridges (an obvious bridge in my city is a large statue of a Roman god overlooking our downtown)? What are the barriers (in my city, the greatest barrier by far is cultural Christianity)? Pray for insight into rightly using those bridges and overcoming those barriers for the sake of the gospel and the good of the people to whom you have been sent.

Week Five: day 3

Exegesis of a Culture

The word exegesis literally means "to draw out" and is applied to the act of studying something (text, art, language) and extracting meaning from it. The opposite is eisegesis (literally "to draw in"), where the observer interprets his findings through his own presuppositions.

Sound theology requires exegesis of Scripture. In order to avoid creating God in our own image, we must glean our understanding of who God is by studying His Word and taking meaning from it. In the same way, sound missiology requires exegesis of culture. Contextual immersion allows us to identify with our audiences and communicate effectively with them. It is much easier to love people who you know and understand.

Unfortunately, exegeting culture can be difficult and time-consuming. Objectivity is impossible, so our tendency is to interpret what we observe in others through the lens of our own presuppositions. When we see something in one culture that brings to mind an evil common in our own culture, it's difficult not to assign that same meaning to the culture we're attempting to study.

Different cultures assign different meanings to various symbols, beliefs, and behaviors. This is called cultural relativism. The only way to learn these different meanings is to become a student of those cultures. This requires deliberately and prayerfully exposing yourself to those things that influence and shape the culture you've decided to study.

Cultural exegesis is a basic missionary skill that allows us to see a peoples' context through spiritual eyes that discern the bridges and barriers to the communication of the gospel. Because culture is dynamic and multi-faceted, it can be difficult to even know where to begin. I recommend you begin exegesis in four key dimensions: story, space, idols, and conflict. While this list is not comprehensive, these four areas are common to nearly all cultures and all places, and provide a great deal of insight into a culture's bridges and barriers to the gospel.

#	Activity
1	Consider "exegesis" versus "eisegesis." In your own words, describe the two concepts. The distinction between them will be important in exercising this skill.

Story

Many Westerners learn history in common fashion—via Hollywood. We learn about *John Adams* from Paul Giamatti in a Tom Hanks-produced HBO miniseries; space history from *Apollo 13*; three presidents, Elvis Presley, and the Black Panthers from *Forrest Gump*; and the horrors of World War II from *Saving Private Ryan*. Come to think of it, we've learned all we know of our history from Tom Hanks.

Sadly, it seems that this is a common phenomenon. Unfortunately, the medium has a tendency to oversimplify. This is why we tend to think in terms of "good guys versus bad guys" or "rags to riches"—it's how the stories are told to us. British literary critic Christopher Booker declared in 2005 there are only seven basic story plots in the world,[19] and our common Hollywood education in history reflects that.

Author Donald Miller says that truth is conveyed through story, not through rational systems.[20] Andrew Jones, missionary, blogger, and global nontraditional church specialist, has often said that his job is to "throw parties and tell stories." Thom Wolf taught that the missionary's role is to retell people's

19 Christopher Booker, *The Seven Basic Plots: Why We Tell Stories* (London: Continuum, 2005), 4.

20 Patton Dodd, "A Better Storyteller: Donald Miller Helps Culturally Conflicted Evangelicals Make Peace With Their Faith," *Christianity Today*, June 2007. Accessed November 2015 http://www.christianitytoday.com/ct/2007/june/10.28.html.

stories back to them in light of the gospel. This is very good missionary tradecraft indeed: find out what people are talking about, and show them how it all relates back to the Most High God.

Every community has a story. The sort of overarching story shaping a culture may not be emblazoned on a plaque in the center of town, but it's no less central to that culture. Its presence is likely more subtle. It can be found in the cautionary tales told by grandparents to their grandchildren. It can be found in the films, books, and viral memes that resonate with members of a tribe. The story may not have a title and probably isn't bound in a book, but members of a culture know the story by heart. It's in the collective consciousness of every member of a group.

#	Scripture
1	Read Luke 18:9-14. How did Jesus retell the Pharisees' own story back to them in light of the gospel He claimed to proclaim (hint: they believed one thing about themselves versus others; He taught another)? The manner in which Jesus approached the Pharisees is good cultural exegesis. He didn't introduce a new story; He retold a familiar one. His audience heard themselves in the story, and realized the story was about them. Even those among them who were neither Pharisees nor tax collectors knew full well what Jesus meant—it's not the outward appearances of religion that God is concerned with; it is their inner contrition and repentance.

#	Scripture, cont.
2	Read John 4:4-26. Again, Jesus retells a familiar story to the Samaritan woman in this passage. How does He turn it to correspond with the gospel He was proclaiming?
3	Are there other passages in Scripture that come to mind in which a common story is retold in light of the gospel? Describe the stories they tell here:

#	Scripture, cont.
4	**Pray** for wisdom as you consider the stories people in your city are telling now. Think of how those stories recall the suppressed memories of the Creator and how you can retell them in light of the gospel. Make notes of any insights as you pray:

Week Five: day 4

#	Activity
1	In your mind, take a walk around your city. "Explore" different neighborhoods and focus on the use of space. How close are the houses to one another? How well are the yards kept? Who lives there—renters or homeowners? Are there toys in the yard? Green spaces in the neighborhoods? How are the houses painted? Are there bars on the doors and windows? Choose a couple of neighborhoods and make a few notes on them here:

Space

Another area for exegesis is the organization, maintenance, and use of space. Levels of trust, social structure, economic systems, and political ideologies can all be discerned through the observation of a people's living arrangements.

Remember: meaning is *drawn out* through observation. The distance between houses, for example, can reveal much about a community, but the reasons a group might share close quarters may not be obvious. Upkeep can give us insight into the demographics of a neighborhood (i.e. young families may have lawns littered with toys; college kids may have lawns littered with beer cans, etc.). Another sign of an aging demographic is visible security.

Residents who own their homes have reason to care for their homes. After all, homeownership is an investment, and property values depend on things like landscaping and curb appeal. Renters, on the other hand, don't have as much incentive to care for things. Mowing the lawn and trimming the hedges is a lot of effort just to maintain someone else's investment. If the leaves are raked and the walkways are swept, it's likely the residents are homeowners.

Being a renter or a homeowner influences a person beyond his investment portfolio. It affects his state of mind. Ownership is a symbol of identification and settlement; these residents have literally bought into the neighborhood. Neighborhoods with higher levels of homeownership tend to be more connected, involved, and secure.

Homeownership is a value for many neighborhoods, but exegesis will reveal whether this is the case in your context. You may find that your neighbors are all renters, or that they see owning a home as participating in an unethical and materialistic system. The point is that you don't know how to best live out the gospel among a people until you've done your research.

Cultural exegesis of the space must extend well beyond just housing. Art and architecture, for example, play a big part in shaping how people understand and interact with their environment. Likewise, modes and patterns of transportation through and across the space can provide terrific insight into a group's attitudes and values. Your observations only tell part of the story. The insight gained through what you see from the outside must be interpreted though the eyes of an insider. You can observe how a community utilizes its space in different ways, but only time and experience can tell you why.

#	Activity
1	Now choose one of the neighborhoods through which you took a mental stroll earlier. What can you conclude about the people living there, in general, through the observations you made in regard to use of space?

Idols

"Man's nature," Calvin wrote in his Institutes of the Christian Religion, "is a perpetual factory of idols."[21] This is evident in the city. Typically, the word idol brings to mind "carved stones of primitive people."[22] But idolatry is much more than bronze statues perched in shrines to the mythological gods.

Human beings can put anything and everything in place of God in their lives. Anything can be an idol, but some things have been made into what theologian Tim Keller has called functional saviors—those things that help even if temporarily to assuage our feelings of guilt before God.

In *Counterfeit Gods*, Keller writes, "It is impossible to understand a culture without discerning its idols."[23] Keller, who is pastor of Redeemer Presbyterian Church in New York City, often speaks about idolatry as the major barrier to the spread of the gospel in a city. He notes that the diversity, restlessness, and tolerance so common in urban areas make them

21 John Calvin, *Institutes of the Christian Religion* (Peabody: Hendrickson, 2007) Book I.XI.8, 1536.

22 Ed Stetzer, The Upstream Collective Jet Set Vision Trip, Istanbul, Turkey, 2010.

23 Tim Keller, *Counterfeit Gods: The Empty Promises of Money, Sex, and Power, and the Only Hope That Matters* (New York: Dutton, 2009), 166.

a breeding ground for idols. Indeed, the Bible often identifies a city by its idols, as in the cases of Sodom, Ephesus, and Athens.

Oftentimes, a city's landmarks acknowledge, commemorate, or even celebrate a district's idols and strongholds. Cultural exegesis must identify the idols that are worshiped throughout the city. Ephesians 6:12 reminds God's people that their true enemy isn't other people: "For we do not wrestle against flesh and blood, but against the rulers, against the authorities, against the cosmic powers over this present darkness, against the spiritual forces of evil in the heavenly places." A stronghold is any argument or high thing that exalts itself against the knowledge of God (2 Corinthians 10:4-5). These may be the lasting memory of wrongdoing, tolerance of sin, the shame of failure, or pride in success.

Potential idols include materialism, sex, power, and wealth. The shrines to these idols are everywhere: shopping malls, billboards, movie theaters, restaurants, and sporting arenas. Oftentimes, idols are wrapped up as a culture's values. Observation and personal interactions will reveal these things and help you see how to show their inadequacy to save.

#	**Homework** due:__________
1	What are the idols in your city? What are they in a particular city to which your church is sending people internationally? What points you to those idols—how do you know what they are?
2	**Pray** for your city and for the places your church is sending. Ask the Lord for insight into the idols there, and particularly how to expose their inability to save.

Week Five: day 5

Conflict

Another significant cultural element in need of exegesis is conflict. In its most basic sense, conflict involves anyone with whom a people may be at odds. Disagreements, aggression, and war are all examples of conflict, but they are never the extent of conflict. People, since the fall of man, are conflicted internally as well as externally; shame, guilt, offense, fear, and hate are universal human emotions.

In order to find these internal conflicts, we need to build on our observations of a people's values. Conflict arises wherever something challenges the values of a people. A group who worships at the throne of consumerism will take on massive amounts of debt in order to maintain their materialistic lifestyle. People who value their political system above everything else will kill to preserve that system. Threats to family, freedom, religion, and control will almost invariably lead to conflict.

Conflict is universal. When exegeting culture, look for signs of struggle. Extreme poverty, war, oppression, protest, and unrest are clear indications of deep social divides. But there are other, less obvious indications of strife. Often celebrated as positive change, gentrification and explosive growth can be serious flash points for conflict between generations, races, social classes, and ideologies. Where there is conflict, there is hurt, frustration, misunderstanding, and ill-will. Listen for heated rhetoric, outrage, and demonization of one party by another.

#	Questions
1	What are a few points of conflict in your city? Where do you see/hear them? How is your church speaking into those areas of conflict?

#	Questions, cont.
2	What are the points of conflict in a city/people to which your church is sending? How have you dealt with those points of conflict as outsiders?
3	Of course, it isn't enough for the missionary to observe signs of conflict. In the midst of conflict, the gospel of peace with God through Jesus Christ is very good news. In order to live as a preview of the Kingdom, we must interject ourselves as peacemakers. Though it might sound counterintuitive, we do this by finding the weak and oppressed and encouraging them not to seek retribution. Thom Wolf sees a pattern of discipleship throughout the New Testament: the weaker side in any conflict is the one with the power to speak peace into the situation.[24] Wolf points out that throughout Paul's epistles, he appeals first to the weaker party in the social dynamic and then to the stronger, urging both to respond to one another with grace and forgiveness.[25] Paul addresses five pairs: wives and their husbands, children and their parents, employee and employer, outsider and insider, and Christian and those who are in authority. In each case, Paul's attention to the minority shows that person's ability to control conflict. The cycle of

24 Thomas A. Wolf, "Urban Social Change" (graduate lecture presented at Golden Gate Baptist Theological Seminary, San Francisco, 1998).

25 Thomas A. Wolf, *The Universal Discipleship Pattern*, (New Delhi, 1992), accessed May 7, 2012, http://tinyurl.com/76n62bb.

#	Questions, cont.
3	aggression is broken when the victim of oppression responds in forgiveness to his oppressor. Cultural exegesis will reveal the person or group of people who can make peace in the face of violence and unrest. How can you/your church be agents of peace within conflict in your city and in the places to which you are sending? How can you bring peace into the particular places of conflict you listed above?

How to Exegete Culture

Cultural exegesis is basic missionary tradecraft. It is a skill learned only through practice, patience, and diligent study. Just as teachers of sound doctrine insist on the thorough study and informed interpretation of Scripture, churches should equip their people to be skilled exegetes of the cultures in which they find themselves.

Observe all that you can. Too often, missionaries turn to books or the Internet for research into the customs and cultures of the people to whom they wish to minister. Much can be learned this way, but nothing compares to the field experience you get from examining culture with your own eyes.

Stories—Listen to local storytellers, read indigenous literature, watch local television and films. Listen for common themes, popular sentiment, and clues into the culture's perspective on identity in relation to God, creation, and the rest of humanity.

Space—Occupy the same space as the people to whom you've been sent. If they gather around campfires, join them. If they hang out in coffee shops, pull up a chair and learn to love coffee. If they live in high-rise apartments, move into the building. To exegete a people's use of space, you must, as far as possible, share that space with them.

Idols—Identify whatever it is that people orient their lives around. Discern what people are afraid of. Find what they worship in the place of the Most High God and begin to develop ways to show and tell people that it is better to worship Him.

Conflict—Look for sources of tension and unresolved conflict. Usually, people establish rules to deal with conflict.

Ask lots of questions. Rather than assume you know why people do what they do, ask them. This will provide opportunities to build relationships and share the gospel. Learn the story, experience the space, identify the idols, and discover ways to stand for peace in the midst of conflict. Record what you observe (it may become clear later how these things are bridges or barriers).

#	Homework due:__________
1	Go practice. Exegete your own city or neighborhood or town. Make note of the history, the personal stories people tell, the use of space, the idols, and the conflict around you. How do those things shape your city and its people? Now do the same thing for a place and people to which your church is sending. If you have not been there yourself, go to the Internet and search for stories, idols, use of space, and points of conflict. Ask those within your church who have been about their experiences there. What can you learn about the people by learning about their culture?
2	**Pray** for your church and the work you are doing in your own city. Pray that you would be wise in understanding the many cultural nuances around you, and that you would learn to read the clues in your city. Pray for those you are sending internationally as they cross cultures. Pray for those who are going to work with them on short-term trips, that they would be good field partners and ready to engage culture wisely. Pray finally for the gospel of peace to take root in the hearts of the people to whom you have been sent, both locally and globally.

Week Five: Group Activity

This week, again, plan a time to work together. Pick a neighborhood to visit. Go together (or split up into teams, if you have a large group) and explore. Try to address each area you studied this week.

Story—find someone who has been in the neighborhood for a long time and simply ask questions. Listen closely to their stories and take note of how they see the city.

Space—what distinct and particular uses of space can you identify within the area? What does the use of space tell you about the people there?

Idols—where are the visible, physical idols, temples, and worship spaces? What are the signs of other unspoken or unrecognized idols?

Conflict—Where are the points of conflict and tension in the neighborhood? Are there neighborhood "rules" to deal with the tension?

Interview people as you explore. Listen to as many stories as you can. Look for varying perspectives on the city.

When you feel you have learned a bit about the culture of the area you have chosen, come back together to discuss your findings. As you do, consider various bridges and barriers to the gospel that may exist for the people there. How might you use and/or overcome them?

If you cannot take a trip together, discuss the areas that you used for the activities on Day 4.

Week Six: day 1

Building Relationships

#	Activity
1	Turn in your Bible to the Gospel of John. Scan the book quickly and note any passages that have anything to do with relationships (God with people and people with one another).

Did you really finish the entire book? If so, you've populated a fairly healthy list of passages that deal with relationships, because the Gospel is all about relationship. And it spreads primarily through relationships. For this reason, we must be committed to both proclaim and demonstrate the gospel through relationship, and we must learn all that we can about relationships in general—how to form them, keep them, grow them, and even end them. Relational tools must be a priority.

Relationship Demands a Bond

There must be something that connects people in relationship, whether good, bad, or indifferent. Blood relation, friendship, life stages, hobbies, affinity, dislikes—all of these are connectors. They are the seeds of relationship.

#	Questions
1	Outside of your familial ties, what are some of the bonds that have tied you to others around you?
2	Did you include any negative ties to poor relationships? "Enemies?" What has bound you to them?

God Is Relational

Theologian, author, and professor Millard Erickson wrote about the effect of understanding God as communal (triune) in his book on Trinitarian theology. He wrote, "It would seem that a first implication would be ... that true personhood involves social interaction, social relationships. To the extent that the individual reflects the image of the Triune God, that individual would not be solitary or independent, but would be related to other persons ... in a particular way."[26]

#	Questions
1	What are some of the ways Scripture describes how God relates to Himself? How does Father relate to Son, Son to Father, and Spirit with Father and Son?
2	How does that shape how we relate to God and how we relate to one another?

26 Millard J. Erickson, God in Three Persons: A Contemporary Interpretation of the Trinity (Grand Rapids; MI, 1995), 332-333.

We relate to God through His incarnate son, Emmanuel—God with us. But we can do so only because Jesus came to us, walked in relationship with us, and experienced every temptation we do. He related to us, so that we can relate to Him. All of it was for relationship, God drawing man unto Himself as a part of his great redemptive plan. Consider the great stories of Scripture—Abraham's call out of Ur, Moses' call to rescue God's people from Pharaoh in Egypt, Joshua's call to take them into the Promised Land, the prophets who spoke for God, Peter's brave obedience in taking the gospel to Cornelius' house, and Paul's defiant demeanor when he determined that he would serve the Lord even in chains. Each of these stories is for the redemptive purpose of relationship—that people would know "the only true God, and Jesus Christ whom [He has] sent."[27] Their purpose is for us to have a redeemed relationship with God.

Building Relationships

#	Activity
1	Believers relate to one another in a familial manner. List out as many Scripture passages as you can that use specific familial terms regarding the interaction of the church, along with the descriptors used.

27 John 17:3.

Unifying Principle

The gospel is the unifying principle for those in the church to relate to one another. We unite as sinners who have experienced the forgiveness of Christ and been cleansed by His blood. We are part of one body, so we should relate to one another as such. Less clear to many within the church, however, is how we are to be in relationship with people who are not believers, people who do not understand or have rejected the basic relational principle upon which our relationships within the body are built. There are diverging approaches on the matter, ranging from isolationism to syncretistic inclusion and everything between. The extremes of this range are obvious theological error, but there is much space between them in which most believers find themselves, and these are often waters not easily navigated.

#	Homework due:__________
1	**Where Are You? Honestly ...** *With an "X," mark where on the continuum you perceive your church to be in how it approaches relationship with those who are not believers. Do you tend toward withdrawing from "worldy" people and activities? Do you tend toward accepting others' habits and practices as your own? Give your mark a name—how you would describe your interaction with outsiders.* *With an "O," mark how those who are not believers view your church's relationship with them. Give it a name—how others would describe your interaction with them. Do they see you as withdrawn from culture? Do they see you as driving culture? Do they see you as antagonistic to culture?* Isolation ⟷ Syncretism Are the two marks in different places on the scale? Why? Describe the differences in perception. According to these perceptions, what are some barriers in building relationships with people outside the church?

#	Homework, cont.
2	Are the two marks in different places on the scale? Why? Describe the differences in perception. According to these perceptions, what are some barriers in building relationships with people outside the church?
3	God prescribed a way that we should interact with each other within His body, and it should inform the manner in which we relate to outsiders, as well. The overarching characteristic was and now remains love (Deuteronomy 6:5; Mark 12:28-34; John 13:33-34). Unfortunately, too often the church's approach is to demand that outsiders live according to a moral code by which they gain relationship to us and, by proxy, to God (i.e. no sex, drugs, or hard rock and we can be friends). Instead of building meaningful relationships with outsiders through which they may see God's character reflected in and through us (imperfect as it may be), we demand a holiness from the world that no one can employ apart from the grace of God. Few of us would ever say that out loud; we just act that way by befriending people who are "less immoral" than others and condemning the "more immoral" for not living up to a code of ethics to which they do not even ascribe. This is a steep divergence from the Jesus we follow who was called a friend of sinners by the "righteous" (Luke 7:34). Describe one good and one bad example of how your church has related to outsiders. What did you learn from each experience?

#	Homework, cont.
4	**Pray** for your church. Pray that you would represent Christ and His love to unbelievers in such a way that they are drawn in, and that you would be called friends of sinners, as well. Pray that you would learn from God's interaction within Himself and with us and make constant application as you form relationships where He has placed you. Pray that you would be wise as you interact within your culture calling people to relationship with God in Christ.

Week Six: day 2

Making Friends Is Good

The people of God are not related solely on affinity but on the common experience of the gospel. We have been forgiven (Colossians 1:14), cleansed (2 Peter 1:9), adopted (Galatians 4:4-7), given new names—a common name (Ephesians 3:15), and sent to represent the One whose name we now bear (2 Corinthians 5:18-20). The Scriptures never demand that we relate to one another (unify) based on the fact that we really like to hang out. We unify around a common Savior and a common mission, neither of which is shared in common with people outside of God's family. So we must be good relationship builders with them based on other external factors.

Being able to make friends is an important tool as we go on mission. Though it sounds simplistic, it is important to note that building relationships is of highest importance, and it does not come all that naturally to a lot of people. The awkward nature of developing friendships causes many people, Christians included, to avoid it. That is not helpful. It is good, then, for us to have a few tools at our disposal as it relates to relationship building. Over the next few lessons, we will explore six tools that are a helpful start.

People are not targets; they are God's image-bearers.

People are not targets for our efforts. Each is made in God's image and therefore worthy of and made for relationship, just as we are. We must be careful to treat them as such. (Maybe, you should read those sentences again; they are terribly important). People, even introverts, need and desire relationships, so relationship-building is a part of who we are as ambassadors (2 Corinthians 5:11-21). Reconciliation requires it.

As we build relationships, we need to take care with our language. The way you label people often determines the way you treat them. Consider a commonly practiced version of evangelism. First, people are "the lost." They hear and believe the gospel and they are labeled "new Christians." They begin to grow and become "people you are discipling." In both local and global mission, it is easy for terms like "souls saved" to portray people in terms of numbers on a ledger sheet. But when do they simply become your friends? When does he move from "some lost guy" to "my friend, Roger?" Jesus certainly thought such a distinction was important. In John 15:15, Jesus said, "No longer do I call you servants, for the servant does not know what his master is doing; but I have called you friends, for all that I have heard from my Father I have made known to you."

His disciples were His friends because He had shared with them the truth. Similarly, our role as ambassadors is to share the truth about God in Christ—to bear witness to the light (John 1:7-8). According to Jesus' words, we do that with our friends, people we love. Words are important. It is not just semantics. Words define things. By our words, we define people. We can either treat them as others worthy of relationship or sentence them to life as a project to be completed. If we choose the latter, our expectation should be that people would respond accordingly. As much as we can do so, we need to avoid labels and categorizations altogether. As soon as we assume that we have someone figured out, we stop learning about him and the relationship is hindered.

#	**Homework** due:__________
1	What do you (within your local church) call people who are not believers around you? Do you think that your label shapes the way you treat them? Positively or negatively? How do you think they would respond if they heard you call them by that label?

#	Homework, cont.
2	How might you or someone else within your church think differently about them if you simply called them by their names?

The gospel should be shared in context of relationship.

Since we are relational creatures in the image of God, the proper context for gospel cultivation is relationship. Often, however, believers ask for this kind of trust from the world without first proving that we really do care—without getting to know them, their hurts, passions, and needs.

In such cases, people aren't necessarily rejecting the gospel so much as they are rejecting the way we are presenting it. If we know nothing about those to whom we are sent; we cannot know how the gospel is good news to them. It is not that we cannot know that the gospel is good news to them, but how. The gospel is always good news, but how it is good to a particular individual depends on who he is. To assume can be dangerous and may even end in an ignorant rejection of truth based on a misunderstanding of what it actually is.

The good news to the Samaritan woman at the well was very different than the good news to the official whose son Jesus healed a few days later (John 4). Each instance was couched in Jesus' understanding of those He was sent to, what their needs were, and what good news was to them. The result in each instance was that the individual to whom Jesus went and his household believed in Him as the Messiah.

#	Activity
1	Brainstorm specific conversations or requests that would produce differing responses based on the relationship between the one asking and the one being asked (i.e. your best friend asks to borrow $10 versus a random guy on the street asking you for the same). List three situations here. Talk about why/how the situation changes based on who is involved. At least one of the situations needs to involve evangelism in some form.

#	Homework due:__________
1	Regarding the way your church refers to unbelievers, does the culture need to change? Would you think about "the lost" differently if you talked about them differently? How could you encourage a shift in thinking and language?

#	Homework, cont.
2	How does your church measure success, specifically in evangelism? Do you talk about it publicly? How do you equip for evangelism? Does it include training in relationship-building? Should it?
3	**Pray** for as many of your "lost" friends as you can think of, by name. Make a list, journal entry, or some other form of notation including all of those people for which you prayed. Write down a bit about who they are and think about how you might know them better. Pray for your church, that you would see others not as targets, but as God's image-bearers.

How-to (continued)

Don't assume you already know—ask questions.

Consider your church's current approach toward missions, both local and global. Would you call it "humble?" In other words, as you approach others with the gospel, whether in your neighborhood or halfway around the globe, is your approach bathed in humility? Read Philippians 2:5-8 and Romans 12:3. Jesus came to earth in complete humility, and Paul admonished the Roman church to watch out for pride.

The Western church's primary approach is often toward apologetics, trying to defend truth through reason rather than offering Christ's love through relationship. A thorough defense of the faith is often needed; but when it occurs in Scripture, it is in opposition to false teaching within the church,[28] not outside.

Our posture toward those outside the church should be one of love, not of antagonism, a position we can quickly assume when we determine that we must prove them wrong in order to win them over. People do not need a defense of God (nor does God, for that matter); they need to experience His character through His representatives. We must be careful not to assume an adversarial position and portray God as adversarial in the process.

One way we can help to ensure the proper posture is by asking questions and listening well to the answers. By doing so, we are able to learn who people are and what good news is to them. We cannot learn about them by prescribing what they need to know. We learn whom people are by asking them to tell us. Then, we listen. They will tell us how we should share the gospel in a manner that is relevant and powerful in their lives.

We must remember that relationships are a long-term investment. They require care and effort to grow. They are two-way, and we cannot force them. Relationships only develop as quickly as both people want to move. No matter how charming, culturally sensitive, and funny we are; no matter how well we listen; no matter how much other people like us, if they don't want relationship, we won't have it. We can only develop our side of the relationship. We must give it time.

Any relationship you might have is a gift from God. He has brought the people in your life to you. Be thankful for those

---

28 Jude 3-4; Acts 15; Galatians 5:1-12.

relationships and be a good steward of those gifts. Spend time praying over them. Think about them and brainstorm creative ways that you might be able to spend more time with them. Learn about the things they like, and take full advantage of the gift of friends (Matthew 25:13-30).

#	Question
1	Can you think of an example in your own life when you have approached a gospel opportunity from a prescriptive viewpoint rather than that of a learner? How did it go? If you could have that opportunity back, would you approach it differently? How so?

Avoid the bait and switch.

Don't be a friend to anyone just so he will become a believer. If people are worth relationship because they are created in God's image, then they are worth it whether they ever follow Jesus or not. We should treat others the way we would wish to be treated, and there is nothing in any of us that wants to endure a relationship with an underlying, unknown, or hidden motive.

"Bait and switch" is dangerous. It builds friendship on false pretense and leaves no room for conversations about really important things without the awkward out-of-nowhere spiritual "attack." As well, it calls into question the validity of the prior relationship. Instead of building relationships on false pretenses, we should be honest about who we are. That does not mean wearing a WWJD T-shirt or giving out "Testamints" all the time. It means living out the character of Christ as prescribed in Scripture, that men may see our good works and glorify our Father in heaven (Matthew 5:13-16).

We do not need to be afraid to fully engage in honest relationship with people—relationship that affords us the opportunity to give account for the hope we have in Christ (1 Peter 3:15). We must be careful, though, not to develop friendships simply as a means to preach, but instead to share "not only the gospel of God, but also our own selves."[29] The people to whom we are sent are worth pouring our lives into, the result of which will be more opportunity for them to see Christ in us and hear the grace-filled words of the gospel proclaimed in our interactions.

#	Questions
1	Can you describe a "bait and switch" methodology regularly employed for evangelism? Have you tried this approach? Know others who have? What is the result?

29 1 Thessalonians 2:8.

#	Questions, cont.
2	Certainly, many "bait and switch" methodologies have been "effective" in the past. Hence, their popularity. Might there be long term unforeseen and unintended effects from the employment of those methodologies?

#	Homework due:__________
1	Define evangelism, as you see it. Does doing your form of evangelism require relationship? Why or why not?

#	Homework, cont.
2	What does humility look like in evangelism? How do you let someone know that you believe they need a Savior in a humble manner? How do you have conversations about God with unbelievers without being antagonistic?
3	Read 1 Thessalonians 2:7-8. **Pray** and ask the Lord that He would help you to be "gentle" among the people to whom He has sent you. Pray that He would turn your affections toward them and that you would freely share not only the gospel but also yourself with them. Pray and consider ways that your church could equip people for just those sorts of relationships.

Week Six: day 4

How-to (continued—again)

Be a blessing.

Maybe being a blessing as you go on mission and build relationships is a given, but I'll go ahead and mention it nonetheless. The result of the original covenant with Abraham was that the world would be blessed through him and his lineage.[30] The fact that we are ambassadors and therefore represent Christ in the world means we are messengers of good news. Good news is in its very nature good for those who receive it. Ambassadors of good news should then bless the people around them. Surprisingly, people who are blessed tend to be open to deeper relationship with the one who blessed them.

Be an interesting person.

#	Activity
1	Imagine for a moment that you are going to meet a man who turns out to be the most interesting person you've ever met. What is he like? What are the traits that make him interesting?

30 Genesis 12:3.

#	Activity
2	Now imagine that the person is a woman. What is she like? What traits are different than the man? What traits are the same?

No one wants to be bored. No one goes to a party and searches for the most boring person there. People like to be with others who tell good stories, enjoy life, and are passionate about something. Christians should be the best at all of those things. We have the best story to tell. Because of that story, we should enjoy our lives immensely. In fact, Jeff Vanderstelt, founding pastor of the Soma Communities, says that Christians should throw the best parties because we have something real to celebrate.[31] Because of these things, our passion for Christ and His kingdom should be evident to those around us. Christians should be creative, fun, passionate, enjoyable, and interesting people. Be one.

Here are a few keys to helping you be interesting along the way:

Be a witness. You don't have a witness so much as you are a witness to the most amazing story in history. You are a witness to the light that shines in the darkness and overcomes it (John 1:7-8). You are a witness of what Jesus has done and, more

31 Jeff Vanderstelt, "Why Throwing Parties is Missional," *Verge Network*, accessed October 2015, http://www.vergenetwork.org/2012/02/10/why-throwing-parties-is-missional-jeff-vanderstelt/.

specifically, how He has redeemed you. That is an incredible story. Tell it in interesting and exciting ways.

Remember people's names. Write them down. Put them in your phone. Carry a little notebook and make notes when you can. Snap a picture with your phone and enter them as a contact in your address book. Do what it takes to remember. Remembering a name shows the value you place on your new friend and helps you gain credibility as you begin to build a new relationship.

Remember the conversations you have had. As important as remembering people's names is remembering who they are, what they do, and anything else they have offered in conversation. If they have trusted you with some information about themselves, don't lightly discard it. Relationship is costly, and most people do not give away information for free. If they see that you've mishandled information they have told you already, they will be far less likely to offer anything new.

Recalling a former conversation and asking for updates is one of the easiest ways to make conversation with a new friend, particularly in the awkward beginnings of relationship. So, remember! If necessary, keep a log of your new friends. Record their name, personal information, and any pertinent information regarding what was going on in their life the last time you spoke with them. If you do so, you can ask about it later and show that it mattered to you.

Pay attention to how you look. If you dress like an outsider, it only stresses the differences between you and those around you. Don't imagine that this difference will only be noticed in another country, either. You are an outsider in any culture other than your own, not just one across an ocean. Even apart from the extremes, tribes tend to have a common style of dress, and in some tribes, the style of dress is important enough to exclude others on its merits. Some differences you may not even notice if you aren't paying close attention can even cause the ones to whom you are sent to be embarrassed to be seen with you. That tends to be a major hindrance to building a relationship. So, do your best to minimize your physical differences and maximize your spiritual ones.

You want tribe members to see the difference in the attitudes and character of a believer, not the differences in appearance between your tribe and theirs. God's call to a new culture might include wearing jeans that don't fit like you like or having to wear your favorite baggy sweatshirt only in the house. Be yourself, but be a version of yourself that embraces the cultural nuance around you.

Being counter-cultural as a believer does not mean being anti-local fashion. It means garnering the character of a believer among people who do not believe. Moses taught the Israelites that developing godly character according to the Law had deep missiological implications. The character of God's people would cause the nations to stand in awe of God's nearness to them and to ask, "…what great nation is there, that has statutes and rules so righteous as all of this law?"[32] Paul taught the same ideas to the church. He said that external cultural things like circumcision or food sacrificed to idols did not determine who they were and could therefore be forsaken or upheld for the sake of mission.[33] What made them counter-cultural, in his estimation was their character, which exposed the state of their hearts.[34] Therefore, we need to be culturally aware enough to dress the part in order to avoid potential roadblocks on mission.[35]

Live among the people, like the people. Jesus came to us, as one of us, in order to relate to us (Philippians 2; Hebrews 4:15). He then sent us out in the same way He had been sent (John 20:21).

Therefore, we enter the culture of the people to whom we are sent. We become like them and live among them. Like Jesus, though, who became like us and lived among us yet without sin, we also do not take part in sin. We take up the pieces and parts of our surrounding culture that are not inherently sinful, such as language, dress, diet, and schedule. An important part of removing barriers to new friendships and doing things like the people around you exposes common interests and makes you more interesting to them.

---

32 Deuteronomy 4:5-8.

33 Galatians 5:2-6; Acts 16:3; 1 Corinthians 8.

34 Galatians 5:16-26; Colossians 3:5-17.

35 More on this in the session, "Contextualization," Week 9.

#	Homework due:__________
1	Simply consider your life and interaction with those to whom you've been sent. Are you interesting? Why or why not? How can you be more interesting, more engaging? In the midst of all of that, how can you be a blessing to those around you?
2	**Pray** that you would be wise, interesting, and a blessing to those in your daily rhythms. Ask God to use those things to help you build relationships with others who need to hear the good news of Jesus.

Week Six: day 5

Conversational Tools

Conversation is a key tool for building relationships. It is important to be able to communicate well who you are, as well as to understand who your new friends are. But conversation is not always easy.

#	Questions
1	What makes a good conversationalist? What is the difference between a good *communicator* and a good *conversationalist*? Are you either of those things? Why?

While the following is certainly not an exhaustive list, here are a few tools to help you as you engage in meaningful conversation.

Listen to the other person instead of just waiting for your turn to talk. One of the most damaging and annoying practices of conversation is when one of the participants is obviously not paying attention, because he is too distracted thinking about what he will say next. Stop it. Listen. Engage. Even if you don't get to say anything, be sure to really care about what your new friend is saying. If you don't pay attention now, you will never remember what he has said to you so that you can further a conversation later.

Pay Attention. Remember that your posture and responses show whether or not you're paying attention. Looking beyond your friend at the television in the corner, losing yourself in the traffic going by, or allowing yourself to be distracted by something on your cell phone are dead giveaways that you are not engaged. Adopt the culturally appropriate posture that communicates that you are listening. The goal is to demonstrate that you care by showing that you are paying close attention.

Read the person you are talking with. If he isn't listening or paying attention to you, stop talking. Notice his body language and don't force anyone to listen to you. You probably know what it is to have someone continue talking when you've lost interest. Pay close attention so you do not do the same thing to him.

Don't just talk about religion. Not every conversation has to be about Jesus. All of your conversations with your other friends aren't, so they don't need to be with your new friends either. Find conversation stimulants about life, common interests, and pop culture. Watch television and movies. Listen to music and read books. Look for truth amid regular conversation. It's also OK to disagree, so you don't necessarily have to avoid touchy or sensitive subjects. Your opinions, thoughts, and actions will all be deeply affected by Christ, so it is OK to talk about them. This does not mean you are not having Christ-centered conversations. Your conversations about family, friendship, work, and social endeavors will all expose the lordship of Jesus in your life and become natural bridges to deeper spiritual conversations.

Be real. Being real is a difficult concept for people who don't already know how. Be honest. Share your thoughts, struggles, concerns, passions, doubts, wins, and losses. People identified with the humanity of Jesus, so we should show ours as well. Don't lie and say everything is all right if it isn't. At the same time don't unload all your troubles on some unsuspecting person. You are supposed to be ministering to them. Your support is found in Christ and His church.

#	Question
1	Given that the above is not an exhaustive list, what other conversational tools would you add to the list? What cues can make people better at conversation?

On Purpose

Living on mission doesn't happen accidentally. It requires intentionality and planning, even practice. Everything you do should leave the mark of Jesus. Show others Jesus' character in your actions. Live among them, and let them in on your life. They need to see, hear, feel, and experience you as you live as a light among them. They need to see you growing in your faith as they begin the journey into theirs. You are fellow travelers.

The ability to build relationships, to be a good ambassador and friend is a necessary part of missionary tradecraft. Some people are gifted with an innate ability to relate to people. Others of us must develop the skill. Either way, it cannot be overlooked as we engage our neighbors and the nations on mission.

#	Homework due:__________
1	Practice. Invite a friend to coffee. Sit at the table with your significant other and chat. Head over to a neighbor's house just to say "hello." Practice good conversational tools.
2	**Pray.** I know it seems strange to ask God to make you better at conversation, but it is key to building relationships for the sake of the gospel. So go ahead and ask for strength, wisdom, and creativity as you develop conversational skills.

Week Six: Questions for Group Discussion

#	Questions
1	What does relationship-building have to do with the Trinity? Discuss the relationships we see represented within the Trinity and how those relationships relate to us.
2	Discuss the familial/relational language used about the church in Scripture. How should this shape the manner in which Christians interact with one another?
3	Discuss the homework activity from Day 1 regarding where you and your church stand in relation to those outside of the church (isolation to syncretism). Compare charts. Note and talk about the differences.

#	Questions, cont.
4	People are not targets; they are image-bearers. Discuss this statement. What does it mean? Why is it important? What is the connection between this statement and how we talk about people outside of the church? Is it merely a semantics issue, or is it something deeper?
5	People aren't necessarily rejecting the gospel so much as they are rejecting the way we are presenting it. Discuss this statement, as well. How might people be open to the gospel but closed to our methodologies of presenting it? Discuss particular examples that come to mind.
6	Discuss the homework from Day 2. Honestly assess your answers. What is common among your answers? What can you learn about the culture of your church from your answers? How might a non-believer view those answers?

#	Questions, cont.
7	What is the connection between mission and humility? How does that play out specifically in the way we pursue relationships with those who do not follow Jesus?
8	Define evangelism as a group. You can use your answers from the homework on Day 3, if you'd like. Does your definition of evangelism require people to build relationships? Why or why not?

#	Questions, cont.
9	Discuss the list of relationship-building how-to's and conversational tools. What would you disagree with? What would you add to the list?
10	Does your church do a good job of preparing people to build relationships for the sake of the gospel? If so, how? If not, how could relationship-building be included as a part of discipleship? Should it be? Why or why not?

Week Seven: day 1

Identifying Persons of Peace

#	Activity
1	Let's say you need a job. You've lost yours, or you are just getting out into the business world from college. Either way, you are searching. Your resume is polished, and you know the type of position you are looking for. In this day of instant connection, how would you begin the search? What steps would you take to find the job you are looking for?
2	At any point in the process, did you include asking friends, family, co-workers, or other people around you if they know of open positions? If one of them tells you of a position, how would you then follow up? Would you ask for a referral? Why or why not?
3	At the outset, even if it appears you are perfect for the position, there may be something more you can do to gain an edge. Knowing someone on the "inside" who can speak on your behalf and refer you to the hiring parties can put you over the top in a pile of equally qualified applicants. In doing so, you gain the one thing a perfect resume can never accomplish—the power of relationship.

Enchufe

In Spain, the word used for this type of relationship is *enchufe*. The literal translation of the word is "plug," but it is used metaphorically to describe a connection or inroad. It implies that one person is "pulling strings" for another and assisting him in achieving the desired outcome. An *enchufe* is a good thing. Jobs, relationships, and various opportunities become reality through the help of a relational connector.

The *enchufe* is common among other cultures, as well. American culture certainly understands the importance of a relational mediator. The reason this concept is a familiar one is simple—relationships define us. We were made for community. "Let us make man in our image," said the One who created all things (Genesis 1:26). As God has eternally existed in relationship, we were made to enjoy and exist in relationship (Mark 12:30-31; John 17:21-23). Jesus even talked about the power of our relationships in revealing the truth of the gospel to the world (John 13:34-35; 17:21-23). The simple reality is that people want to be in relationship with other people, and existing relationships are powerful tools for creating new relationships. They are often leveraged[36] for creating opportunities that otherwise would not have existed. As the adage goes, "It's not what you know but who you know that matters."

Describe three circumstances (other than a job search) in which you might look for a referral:

36 Leverage is a terrible word to use when speaking of relationship. However, it is the right word to use in this case, as long as we stray from a distinctly utilitarian understanding of the term. In its simplest form, it means to use for gain. People often meet other people through existing relationships. Understanding that to be so, we can take advantage of the process—not the people—and intentionally use existing relationships to build other relationships. I am not advocating we use people simply to find an avenue to other friends. I am instead suggesting that we understand how relationships breed other relationships and allow this natural avenue to develop fertile soil for the gospel. That is not utility; it is friendship and stewardship.

Person of Peace

People often depend on relationship over and above conventional wisdom. Based on the recommendation of others, we will be open to something or someone we otherwise would not have considered. Advertisers know this to be true, hence all the recognizable faces and stories in ads and commercials. Businesses know it to be true, as well. Think of all of the referral programs offered by banks, credit card companies, and cell phone services. These programs make our friends spokespeople for their products and services. They work because we are made for relationship, and our relationships deeply influence the decisions we make.

Relationship determines what and whom you believe, as well. You trust the local mechanic because your brother-in-law, who you trust already, told you he was trustworthy. Your neighbor's wonderful recommendation of her dermatologist has you filling out crossword puzzles in his waiting room. You even allow your best friend's high school buddy who is now a missionary in Bangladesh to share with your family about what it means to follow Jesus, trusting all the while that your friend was right about him. You make all of these decisions based primarily on the reputation and referral of your friends and family, and you are not alone in this practice.

Relationship is currency, and there is always a broker.[37] There is always someone who oversees the transaction and on whose word and reputation the exchange hangs. In Luke 10, we read the story of Jesus sending out the 70 (or 72, depending on the translation). Verses 5-9 are as follows

> *5 Whatever house you enter, first say, 'Peace be to this house!' 6 And if a son of peace is there, your peace will rest upon him. But if not, it will return to you. 7 And remain in the same house, eating and drinking what they provide, for the laborer deserves his wages. Do not go from house to house. 8 Whenever you enter a town and they receive you, eat what is set before you. 9 Heal the sick in it and say to them, 'The kingdom of God has come near to you.'*

---

37 Here again is a strange term for this conversation. *Currency* most commonly has an ascribed utilitarian/financial meaning. It is defined as a medium of exchange, which can have a plethora of meanings. As with my use of leverage, we do not promote using people. We do not form a relationship with person A in order to access person B. However, being in relationship with person A may yield the fruit of connection with person B.

In this passage, we are introduced to the powerful concept of a person of peace in missional advancement. Jesus prescribed a particular manner in which His followers should approach unfamiliar communities and local cultures. His plan was for His people to go into a town and proclaim the same message the angels proclaimed at Christ's birth—the gospel—the good news of the advent of the kingdom of peace. They would then wait for a response, and act accordingly.

If a positive response was given, the follower of Jesus would set up camp in the house of the respondent and work among the community from his vantage point. A negative response required a pronouncement that God's kingdom had indeed been near and a warning that refusal to acknowledge that truth and receive the kingdom had dire consequences.[38]

If a son of peace was indeed found, the disciples were instructed to stay with him,[39] eat and drink what was set before them, and not bounce around from place to place. They would dwell there and represent God's kingdom well within that home. It would be from that home that their ministry within the town would be done.

---

38 This particular instruction from Jesus for the disciples He was sending out can also be found in Matthew 10:11-14 and Mark 6:10-11.

39 We have chosen to use the ESV version of the Bible for quotations within this workbook. The ESV translates the Greek word υιος as son, which is a perfectly acceptable translation of the word (though other translations use person of peace, peaceful person, or person who promotes peace). There are, however, many uses of the word in the New Testament, some representing familial connection, some connoting maleness, some speaking of friends, some speaking broadly about people who act a certain way. It is not a term that necessarily means male offspring (there are several other Greek words that mean direct relation). υιος is a term that stresses the character of the relationship. It seems in Luke 10 that Jesus means to express the nature of the relationship. The son of peace is one who would relate to the sent one as a family member would; they would be accepted, cared for, and taken in as if they belonged to the family of the person of peace. Looking at the examples throughout the New Testament of people who seem to fall into this category, we do not find it helpful to designate the particularly male term son for the role. Since it is not used only to delineate maleness in Scripture, we find the use of the term person of peace to be appropriate. For more information on this please refer to: W.E. Vines, An Expository Dictionary of New Testament Words (Old Tappan, New Jersey: Fleming H. Revell Company, 1966) Vol 1, p.187; Vol 4, p.47.

#	Questions
1	Why would Jesus direct His disciples to dwell with the person of peace? What role would that play in their work? What advantages (if any) might they be afforded by the practice?
2	How is this directive still applicable today (if at all)? Should you preach the gospel and then move in with anyone who responds? What, in your view, would be the advantage of a person of peace in mission?

#	**Homework** due:__________
1	**Read** Luke 8-11 to understand more fully the context of the passage in which Jesus directed His followers regarding the person of peace. As you read, simply **pray** for understanding. Ask God to open your eyes, ears, and heart as you read the words and actions of Jesus. Write down any insight you find in context or any thoughts you may have regarding how the concept of a person of peace might apply today.

Week Seven: day 2

So, What Is a Person of Peace, Anyway?

Jesus certainly knew that people were made for relationship. It was, after all, Jesus who made them that way. So, His admonition to His followers in Luke 10:5-9 was to leverage relationship for the sake of the mission through the person of peace. Since this person was of great importance to Christ, we need to endeavor to understand what exactly a person of peace is and why he or she was so important.

Thomas Wolf defines the person of peace:

> 'Person of peace' is a Hebraism meaning "one inclined to peace" (Plummer 1909:273). A person of peace is someone or some group sovereignly prepared by God to receive the gospel.[40]

The person of peace is one already primed, by grace, through the work of the Spirit to receive the good news of Jesus. The presence of such a person speaks to God's sovereignty, having prepared beforehand those who would be saved and softening an otherwise hard heart to the gospel message. It also speaks to our need to proclaim the gospel in word and deed on a wide scale, seeing that we are not privy to God's sovereign plan and do not know whom He has called. Again, from Dr. Wolf:

> Before you ever make contact, before you ever meet her, before "Peace" is spoken to him, the person of peace has been prepared by God: that person has, within his own life time, among the boundaries of his own life, groped and grappled with self, sin, society, existence, so that the One in whom he lives and continues being has spoken to his inner heart and written codes of truth in such a way that that person, that person of peace, will be born afresh by the word preached. And in the most unpromising of circumstances, wherever there is a person of peace, Christ will enter in.[41]

40 As you will note throughout this chapter, much is made here of Dr. Wolf's writing. That is, in part, because there is very little writing on the subject of the person of peace. It is also in large part due to the fact that Dr. Wolf has taught it so well. Whereas there are hints of the topic mixed in with other people's writing, I am unaware at the time of this writing of any extensive work based on the idea. In fact, a Google search for Person of Peace will yield a pdf file of some of Dr. Wolf's teaching on the matter as the No. 1 result. Thomas A. Wolf, "Persons of Peace," accessed September 2015, http://www.kncsb.org/resources/PersonsofPeace.pdf.

In your own words, define a person of peace. How would you describe this person to someone else?

Jesus couches the teaching in Luke 10 regarding a person of peace in the midst of a much larger story and a great deal more teaching about His mission and how it will be carried out. Two chapters earlier (Luke 8), Jesus tells a story about sowing seed that infers a broad spreading of the seed, not necessarily a particular and painstaking choice about good soil, bad soil, weeds, or other particular dangers that inhibit the gospel's taking root. We see here, again, that we are not privy to who is and who is not called by God and that widespread commendation of the kingdom is good and necessary.

Following the parable of the sower, however, Jesus speaks about lighting a lamp and not hiding it away, so that *whoever enters the home* will see it. It is a much more personal approach and one that Jesus echoed as He sent out the 70. Both a widespread witness and personal relationships are important to the spread of the gospel message. The broad witness of the follower of Jesus was important, in part, because it would lead to finding the person of peace.

The Person of Peace Is Not the Goal

The disciples were not sent out to find the person of peace. They were sent to proclaim the gospel of the kingdom. God then used their proclamation to reveal the persons of peace that He prepared beforehand. If their focus was finding the person of peace, it may have very easily translated into a project of sorts—a selective process of sorting through people to find "the one." We find in Jesus' directions a command to speak peace and move accordingly as the hearers respond.

Numerous missionaries have embarked on a person of peace "Easter egg hunt" of sorts. They have gone into a new place and bounced from person to person with no concern for relationship, simply asking some church- or faith-related question to complete strangers. Asking a teacher in a new place if you can conduct a church function in her school does not equal speaking peace to her and can sometimes actually be damaging to your reputation and cause.

---

41 Ibid.

#	Questions
1	What is "speaking peace?"
2	How does that differ from searching for a person of peace?

What Does It Mean to Be Received?

Our expectation of what it means to be received shapes the way we approach the process of gospel proclamation. Judaism, the religion of the people to whom Christ sent His followers, of course, was well known for its hospitality as commanded in Scriptures (Leviticus 19:34, Exodus 12:49), which was well documented throughout Israel's storied history.[42]

Hospitality was a foregone conclusion among the Jews. However, Jesus' followers were preaching something new, a fulfillment to the expectations of the Jews leading to that point. Some would receive the message, and some would be hostile to it—maybe violently so. It was a frightening endeavor, trusting that their provision would come through the kindness of others. It was also a deeply exciting, encouraging, and faith-building one, knowing that certainly people would respond to the gospel of peace and their needs would be met through their work as ambassadors for Christ's kingdom. Simply not being thrown out on their ears would be a sign that God was at work.

#	Questions
1	What would it have meant for the disciples to be received? Not received?
2	What does it mean for you now to be received by someone as you proclaim the gospel?

42 Abraham eagerly hosted three strangers in Genesis 18; Lot cared for his three visitors in Genesis 19 so vigorously that he offered his two virgin daughters for their protection; Laban hosted a stranger in Genesis 24; David was received and cared for in 2 Samuel 17:27-29; a wealthy couple built on a room for Elisha in 2 Kings 4; and Job wrote that he had been faithful to care for the sojourner in Job 31:32, et al ...

People Respond Differently

People, even persons of peace, will respond differently in varying places and cultures. Some may be immediately responsive, like Cornelius in Acts 10. Others may require some persuasion, such as the ones who join Paul and Silas in Acts 17:4. There may be people in certain cultural contexts who move toward faith fairly easily and immediately respond to the Holy Spirit.

On the other hand, there may be those that God is calling out of a post-Christian or other difficult context who require a bit more relational connection before they open themselves to religious conversation. The simple fact that they are open to relationship with you is cause for celebration. They still may be gatekeepers into their community, even though the process is slower than with others.

Jesus did not send out the 70 with a mission to find a particular few who would be persons of peace, per se. He had sent them out to represent the kingdom and proclaim its message, which would inevitably lead them to those whom God had prepared, immediate or not. However, once the person of peace responded, the relationship birthed was leveraged to its fullest, to the extent that he and his household would become the center of the ministry happening in his community.

The person of peace became a sort of gatekeeper into the community to which he belonged. He became a referral for the believer to his friends and family. He became the broker of the currency of relationship. If you look back to Luke 10, you will see that Jesus told the 70 that once the person of peace emerged, they were to move in and receive the hospitality offered them (Luke 10:7-8). They were to basically join his household, at least temporarily; and through the relationship they were to become an acceptable outsider among the people of the community (Luke 10:9).

#	**Homework** due:__________
1	Refer back to the questions and answers from Day 1 and consult any notes you may have made. With a bit more information now, begin to chart out what advantages may be found in working with a person of peace. Think about receptivity to the gospel on their part as well as receiving hospitality on your part. How do the two work together as you enter into new mission fields (whether in your hometown or across the globe)?
2	What are the potential road blocks you see in you and/or your church engaging in ministry through people of peace within certain communities of people? How might you address those issues?
3	Receiving hospitality is often more difficult than offering it. Spend some time **pray**ing that you and others in your church would not only be hospitable, but would receive hospitality graciously for the sake of the gospel.

Week Seven: day 3

So, What Is a Person of Peace, Anyway?

It's Spiritual ...

Finding the person of peace is not a science. It is in its very essence spiritual. When we go, we are not looking for a person; we are awaiting the Spirit of peace within a person that will lead them to respond to the gospel. Through the revelation of the person of peace, we are given a divine hint that we are indeed among the people to whom we have been sent and God has prepared the way for gospel harvest.

Using common sense and logic, describe the type of person you think might most often be the person of peace in a community.

Our tendency toward the tangible leads us to develop systems, however—the person of peace will have qualities A, B, C, and D. We begin to look for the qualities we have determined to be essential instead of listening to the Spirit and following His leadership to someone who is actually overcome with the Spirit of peace and open to the gospel.

A common conception of a person of peace is someone who seems relationally well-connected. If someone is going to rely on the relationships of the person of peace for the transmission of the gospel, then he would want to find someone with far-reaching connections. Strangely, though, Jesus commonly called the outcast to Himself. The disciples were not rock stars in their communities. They were physical laborers and not known for their intellect. Matthew was probably hated by most that knew him. Simon was a zealot and likely had plenty of enemies. Jesus even used a demoniac who was living naked, alone, and chained in a graveyard to reach His community.

Here again we see the importance of the Spirit's leadership in mission. We must not rely only on man-made strategies for finding the people with whom we should tie ourselves for the work of ministry. It is the Spirit who called us; it is the Spirit who guides (Galatians 5:25).

That said, there are three marks of the person of peace we need to consider that have more to do with their spiritual response than personality traits, beginning with their own openness to the gospel.

Marks of the Person of Peace[43]

1. **Receptivity**

The person of peace responds to the gospel (Luke 10:6). As we have previously noted, it may be an immediate or delayed response, but he responds. He or she is the first within the community or tribe to respond to the gospel and becomes the beginning point or conduit for the rest of the ministry there.[44]

Our natural process of evangelization is to sow first and reap the returns afterward. However, the idea of the person of peace is that God has sovereignly gone before the ones He has sent and prepared the heart already. The seed of the gospel has already been sown (John 4:38). The sent one goes into the harvest not to sow, but to reap the person of peace.

In Luke 10:2, Jesus made it clear that the harvest was plentiful, and there was work to be done. The missing part of the equation was not the ones whom God had sovereignly prepared for response to the gospel; it was those who would work among them. One cannot overlook Jesus' point in the verse—there are those who will respond. Yet, as we noted earlier, those He sent did not know who or where they were, or when they might respond. Jesus' words, then, were meant to be an encouragement for His followers; there would be fruit in their effort. Some people would receive them, thereby receiving Christ (Luke 10:16).[45]

There are a couple of pitfalls to avoid with this idea. The first pitfall lies in the idea that fruitfulness—people responding to the gospel—proves both the call and faithfulness of the one who is sent. To be clear, the work of the follower of Christ

---

43 Ibid., Wolf.

44 The conversion of Cornelius and his household (Acts 10), Lydia and her household (16:14), and the Philippian jailer and his household (16:30-33) are all wonderful examples of this idea. These people had their hearts opened by the Lord. God had done the work. The apostles only had to enter the field and reap (Just as Jesus said in Luke 10, "the harvest is plentiful." The sowing was already done). Once the person of peace emerged, her *oikos*—or household, including extended family, friends, and others in the house—was always converted, as well, and became an entry point to the rest of the community (i.e. Peter remained with Cornelius working from his home for some days; Lydia opened her home to Paul and Timothy from which they worked in Philippi and through which the Philippian jailer was converted).

45 Here, I have made a case for reaping where we have not sown. The existence of a person of peace does not remove from the believer the responsibility of sowing the seed of the gospel; it only offers a platform from which to do so. The person of peace really is a gift. He is a harvest for which we have not worked, but in his company begins the work of sowing inside his relationships (Luke 10:7-9).

is simply obedience—going as Christ has sent him. Drawing men unto Himself is something only God can do (John 6:28-29, 44). Obviously, Jesus expected there would be people who would not receive the gospel, hence His instructions for just such an occurrence in Luke 10:10-11. We only go in obedience to Christ's call; God gives the increase (1 Corinthians 3:7).

The second pitfall, closely related to the first, is the mistaken notion that responsiveness dictates our strategy. In other words, we go only where people are visibly responsive to the gospel. That is obviously not what Jesus was telling His followers. He told them they would experience rejection and go to places where people would not respond positively. We should expect some of the same.

As Jesus sends us under the leadership of the Spirit, we are to go to whom He has sent us with the message of good news He has given us regardless of the responsiveness of the people. Matthew Henry wrote of this idea, "They must show, not only their goodwill, but God's good-will, to all to whom they came, and leave the issue and success to him that knows the heart."[46] Again, people's responses are not our responsibility. Our obedience to Christ's call is. Otherwise, we find ourselves in disobedience and may even miss the opportunity to sow where others may later water and reap (John 4:37; 1 Corinthians 3:5-9).

What, in your opinion, could be the result of falling into one or the other of these pitfalls?

2. **Reputation**

The person of peace is not just any convert. Instead, she is a person with a reputation, well-known by those among her family, friends, neighbors, and co-workers—her *oikos* (Luke 10:9). Be careful here, though, because she is not necessarily always a person of good reputation.

Then again, now the person might well be a person of high reputation, as were Cornelius, Lydia, the Ethiopian eunuch,

46 Matthew Henry, "Complete Commentary on the Whole Bible: Luke 10," Study Light, accessed September 2015, http://www.studylight.org/com/mhc-com/view.cgi?book=luchapter=010.

and others. But consider the demon-possessed slave girl with the spirit of divination (Acts 16:16), or the Gerasenes man among the tombs with an unclean spirit. No one was able to bind him anymore. But everyone knew of him. He was a person of reputation, and he manifested himself to be a person of peace.[47]

Missionaries entering a new culture or community often try to begin by finding the people who are "closest" to being Christians. They find the ones who are living by some moral and ethical standards that reflect "goodness." They look for the good people, because it seems they are the easiest ones to help bridge the gap and believe the gospel. That is not always the case, and God may call the "worst" among them in order to show His power and glory. In fact, He may cause the foolish to shame the wise (1 Corinthians 1:27).

What are a few examples of people with bad reputations in Scripture who became persons of peace? Who are others in modern history or your own circles?

What are a few examples of people with good reputations in Scripture who became persons of peace? Who are others in modern history or your own circles?

3. **Referral**

The person of peace refers the gospel through influence via existing relationships (Luke 10:7-9). As we have seen in the previous examples, these relationships are a conduit for mission. As we "take up residence" with them and work from their vantage point, we gain an audience with whomever they already had an audience.

---

47 Wolf, "Persons of Peace."

To help understand referral, we can examine the communal nature of fish. All fish school, and they are led as they swim by what scientists call fish of reference. Those fish initiate every turn within the school. It turns and the others follow. The person of peace acts in the same manner as the fish of reference, in effect, turning first in his tribe and leading others to follow.[48]

Just as the school of fish needs one to turn first so that others can follow, groups of people, or tribes, also need someone to lead out by turning first. An outsider seldom turns an entire tribe. His best hope is to become an acceptable outsider who is brought into the tribe through relationship with the person of peace. This person of peace, then, is of utmost importance to the missionary as she builds new relationships and takes the gospel to new people and places, whether in her own hometown or around the globe.[49]

Apart from mission, where have you seen this principal in action?

How might referral aid you in your mission efforts?

48 Wolf, "Persons of Peace."

49 By missionary, I mean to say Christian, not just full-time Christian worker. All followers of Christ are meant to join Him on mission (Matthew 28:18-20; Acts 1:8, et al.) thereby making them missionaries. This tool is important for an American marketplace worker in Europe, a full-time Chinese Christian worker in the Middle East, and someone living on mission in the same city where he grew up.

How might dependency on the referral of others inside a community hinder your efforts in mission? How might you adjust those efforts to change referral from a hindrance to a help?

#	Homework due:__________
1	If engaging a person of peace in your mission efforts is a new concept for you, read back through the passage again. Scan through examples found in the Gospels and the book of Acts. Make a list of examples here (hint: there are several listed in this lesson).

#	Homework, cont.
2	How do you think this often misunderstood and overlooked concept could change the manner in which you/your church engage in mission? Should it? Is this passage merely descriptive language letting us know how Jesus sent His disciples out; or is it prescriptive for us, as well?
3	Persons of peace, as seen throughout the New Testament, can be a source of much help in reaching the lost. As you consider this Scripture and concept, **pray** for insight as to how you might engage in mission using this powerful gift God has given us to engage in His mission. Rejoice in the fact that there are those whose hearts have been prepared to receive Him. Rejoice in the fact that you are privileged to carry the life-changing good news to those who will!

Week Seven: day 4

Posture

What should be the posture, the attitude of a missionary entering a new culture (whether in his neighborhood or another country)? How should he or she approach the people there (particularly according to Jesus' teaching on the person of peace)?

As we form new relationships on mission, our posture is important. The manner in which we approach people often determines the manner in which they respond. Therefore, it is imperative that we maintain a posture of humility and vulnerability. Jesus sent His followers into the harvest without much provision, leaving them fully dependent on the people to whom they were sent. He also warned them they would face rejection, but they could not take it personally. Both of these things required them to lay down pride and self-dependence and approach the people to whom they were sent in humility and thankfulness.

Mission is often portrayed as one person who has something that another person needs, offering it to him as a solution to his "problem" and a means to garner an audience for gospel proclamation. This is not inherently a bad thing. The problem comes in the posture of the missionary and has everything to do with pride.

I know of an American church that felt called to work in a particular area of Spain. They decided their point of entry into the culture would be through hosting soccer camps for children. Of course, soccer is immensely important in Spain. There are real soccer players there. Every kid in Spain grows up playing the game and playing it well. Even so, this group coming from the United States where soccer is not all that big a deal, wanted to teach Spanish children to play the game they already loved.

A wise missionary counseled the church instead to join a Spanish-led soccer camp and learn from them. Changing the way they chose to approach the people would change their posture. Instead of coming in with all the answers which would have very likely turned off the Spanish people they hoped to know, he encouraged the church group to lower its posture, which would likely lower the guard of the people from whom they were learning. They would move from a perceived air of pride as the teachers to humility as learners.

Jesus Came Humbly ...

Paul wrote of Jesus in Philippians 2 that "He made himself nothing" and "humbled Himself to the point of death, even death on a cross." Christ came in the most humble form He could have, as a baby, with no way to fend for Himself and completely dependent on the hospitality of the ones to whom He came for His survival. Some accepted Him well, while others did not.

Christ's humility was not an accident but a purposeful choice, and one that He taught His followers to make as well.[50] In Luke 10:3-16, Jesus again asked His followers to become subservient and lower themselves to be dependent on those to whom they were sent. Approaching people this way would make it easier to combat their natural sinful pride. Jesus gave His followers a continual reminder to constantly bear their cross well and walk in humility. The good news they offered was the same good news offered them by Christ; and it was not of themselves, it was the free gift of God, not of works, lest they (we) should boast (Ephesians 2:8). Remember that the way we approach people often determines the way they react. So, we must be careful how we approach others as we follow Jesus on mission.

#	Question
1	Consider the local and global mission efforts you and/or your church are involved in. List a few of the strategies you employ within those efforts (i.e. teaching classes, medical services, construction, etc.). Beside each of those strategies, write a bit about your posture as you engage. How are you perceived by the people there? How do you ensure that your approach is one of humility and thankfulness? How can you receive hospitality from the people to whom you go?

50 Matthew 16:24; 18:1-4; 20:16; 20:26-28, et al.

Person of Goodwill

Pertinent to the conversation is another idea about a person who can also be quite helpful as we go on mission. He is commonly called the person of goodwill. There are several instances of the person of goodwill in Scripture, although this title is never explicitly stated.[51]

A person of goodwill is one who shows the follower of Christ kindness along the journey, because God has turned his heart toward the missionary. It may even be only for a little while. The differentiating characteristic between the person of peace and the person of goodwill is the transformational change in their lives. The person of peace changes from one who does not follow Jesus into one who does. That is not the case for the person of goodwill.

The person of goodwill can be an invaluable resource for the modern missionary, as well. He may come in the form of:

- a non-believing business owner who knowingly allows believers to meet in his business;
- an unbelieving immigrations officer who helps a missionary figure out how to stay in country and what paperwork needs to be filled out to do so;
- a border control agent who searches a missionary's bags and somehow doesn't notice the suitcase full of Bibles in the van;
- a political leader who suddenly, and maybe momentarily, loosens control of the people who can legally enter the country;
- an unbelieving city official who opens the door for believers to work in their own city in places and ways they have not been allowed before.

Our tendency may be to try to find the border control or customs agent after our encounter with them and share the gospel. If led by the Spirit to do so, then certainly sharing with them is the right thing to do. However, it may be that God is simply directing the agent according to His will for our good and His purposes. These people may never follow God or even recognize the role they have played in advancing His mission.

---

51 Cyrus in Ezra 1:2-4; Darius and Artaxerxes in Ezra 6-7; Artaxerxes in Nehemiah 2:1-8, et al.

#	Homework due:__________
1	Can you name instances in which you/your church engaged in some mission effort out of what might have been perceived as a prideful posture? How might you have gone about it differently to ensure humility? Do you think people's response might have been different?
2	Can you think of people who might have functioned as people of goodwill for you/your church on mission? How were they used by God? What was your response to their involvement?

#	Homework, cont.
3	Read back through the passage in Luke 10 and consider carefully Jesus' instructions to the disciples. The way He sent them out required them to take on a posture of humility. On purpose. No matter our strategy in mission, it is imperative that we do the same. We mirror the character and posture of Christ as we join Him on mission. As you read, **pray** that God would give you insight into your missional posture and wisdom on how to ensure humility. Pray for your church, that there would be no strategy devised that would hinder your ability to walk in humility. As you think and pray, jot down any thoughts you have here.

Week Seven: day 5

#	Activity
1	We have seen the principle of the person of peace in Scripture, but the specifics of its application are less clear. Before moving ahead, take a little time to think through process and strategy. Now that you understand the instructions of Jesus to work through the person of peace, how would you use the information? What would you do to start engaging people in order to find the person of peace?

What Now?

First, foremost, and continually—pray (1 Thessalonians 5:17). Jesus directs His followers to do so as He sends them into the harvest (Luke 10:2). He tells them to ask the Lord to send laborers into the harvest. It is God who sends people out. It is also God who determines when and how they go. Central to the engaging the person of peace, as with every aspect of Christian life and mission, is prayer.

Finding the people God has appointed and prepared to receive the gospel and its messengers is not an easy task. A systematic approach to finding persons of peace usually does not yield results. Therefore, our approach must be less "strategic" and more spiritual in nature. Again, we do not know the ones God has prepared for our coming, but we trust that He does. We must follow the encouragement we find in Scripture to simply ask God, who responds when we ask.[52] He will lead us as we pray and he will speak for us as we go (Luke 21:14-15).

Secondly, after we pray or as we continually pray, we move among the relationships God births. As He leads us to a person of peace, we are to dwell with him. This does not necessarily mean moving into the garage apartment. It means living life together, knowing who they know, and working within the existing relational structures around them.

In providing us with persons of peace, God is clearing the way for a relational transfer of the gospel along pre-existing lines. If we do not use the relationships He gives us through the persons of peace, we will be blazing a new trail when He has already cleared one for us. These people are clear paths to the relationships around them; therefore, we dwell with them and enjoy the gift of God by which the gospel finds its way into new communities.

Thirdly, we must know when it is time to move on. Just as Jesus prescribed the method by which His followers would enter a town and stay when received, He also prescribed how they would leave a town that rejected them (Luke 10:10-15). They would certainly face rejection, trouble, and danger (John 16:33; 17:14). The real question dealt not with if they would struggle but how they would handle struggles when they came.

To teach them how they should respond in this situation, Jesus reminded His followers they were not actually the ones people would be rejecting (Luke 10:16). They would be ambassadors sent to the people in someone else's name. People's rejection would not be of the sent ones, but of the sender, the One in whose

52 1John 3:22; Matthew 7:7-8; James 1:5.

name they would come. The people would actually be rejecting God. Jesus' admonition was to either find the person of peace and dwell with him, or to recognize decisive rejection and move on (e.g. Acts 13:51; 17:1-14; 18:4-11).

#	Questions
1	How do you handle rejection? What is your default response when someone rejects the gospel you have presented? How can you combat the natural tendency toward offense?
2	How do you graciously respond to someone who rejects the gospel? What does humility look like in that situation?

Be Careful ...

We need to be very careful when it comes to moving on. Luke 10 does not say that we should make a quick gospel presentation, listen for a response, and move on if the hearer does not immediately come to faith. In fact, in reading the book of Acts, we see the early church being soundly rejected, imprisoned, beaten, and stoned, only to return right back to the same city to continue preaching the same gospel.[53] Apparently, the early church did not see those moments as decisive rejection, because they returned to the places and people who mistreated them.

On the other hand, we also see situations in which moving on was the necessary choice. One such occasion occurred in Antioch in Pisidia and is found in Acts 13. Paul boldly preaches the gospel in the synagogue on the Sabbath and many Jews respond. They beg Paul and Barnabas to return the next week, which they do, and most of the city shows up to hear the gospel. Some of the Jews began to argue with them, so Paul turned his attention to the Gentiles and many believed.

Even so, the Jews and other officials drove Paul and Barnabas out of the city. Acts 13:51 recorded that Paul and Barnabas "shook off the dust from their feet against them." There was successful work within the city. People believed and yet Paul and Barnabas moved on. Neither of these situations seems to jibe with Jesus' instruction to stay where we are received and shake off the dust from our feet when we are not, so there must be a spiritual element to the process.

The disciples received the Holy Spirit, and it was the Spirit, whom Jesus had sent who was leading them, telling them where and when to go or not to go (Acts 13:2; 16:6-10; 18:9-11, et al). In the same way, the Spirit leads us as we go. Many people prefer black and white strategies. The tension of operating inside the gray is difficult. It would be easiest to have a very clear if/then chart for when and where to go on mission, but that would lessen the importance of knowing and hearing God.

Certainly, Jesus gave us a strategy—go where we are welcomed and leave where we are not. The difficult part is we may not always know exactly what it means to be welcomed or exactly when we are being rejected. The lesson we must learn here is that planning and strategy are important and excellent tools as we go. However, we must hold loosely to our plans and strategies in favor of the leadership of our Lord. It is He who will lead us down the natural avenue for taking the gospel to a new culture; the person of peace, and it is He who will lead us away to the next one.

---

53 Acts 4:3, 18-21; 5:17-21, 40-42; 14:19-21, et al.

#	Homework due:__________
1	Have you/your church ever experienced the Spirit's direction to continue working among people who seemed to be rejecting the gospel? Have you ever been directed to leave when it seemed people were responding? How did you handle these situations? Were you able to easily step away from your strategy, or did you struggle to hold on to it?
2	Simply **pray** for yourself and your church that you would be both humble and wise as you engage in mission. Pray that God would lead you to those who are prepared to receive the truth of the gospel.

Week Seven: Questions for Group Discussion

#	Questions
1	What is an *enchufe*? In what situations would such a relational mediator be useful?
2	Read Luke 10:1-9 together. Is this passage merely descriptive (describing an interaction between Jesus and His disciples), or is it prescriptive (giving direction useful for all of His followers to come)? Why?
3	Referring back to the questions from Day 1, what would be the advantage(s) of "dwelling" with the person of peace? What does the missionary gain through this relationship?

#	**Questions, cont.**
4	Define the person of peace. Discuss commonalities/differences in your understanding of the concept. Talk about examples from Scripture.
5	What could be possible outcomes of engaging in the search for a person of peace as opposed to "speaking peace" and waiting for a response? What is the difference?
6	How have you/your church engaged in relationships with persons of peace? Tell a few stories.

#	Questions, cont.
7	Name and discuss the three marks of the person of peace.
8	How does the posture of the missionary affect the ones to whom they are sent? What is the correct posture and why?
9	What is a person of goodwill? How does this person differ from a person of peace? Talk about examples from Scripture and any that you have experienced or heard of in modern mission.

Week Eight: day 1

Engaging Tribes

What images are conjured in your mind when you read the word "tribe?" There are surely some preconceptions when it comes to that word. Do you imagine a small village in some remote area devoid of power, running water, and other modern conveniences? Maybe you picture groups of natives living, farming, and hunting in those villages. A Google search on the word yields a plethora of results, from a social networking site to an advertising agency to photos of African tribesmen to fans of the Cleveland Indians to a book by Seth Godin.

The way we think of tribes is changing. Had Google existed 30, 40, or 50 years ago, the search results would have been very different. They would have been far more narrow in scope, focusing mainly on indigenous people groups.

#	Activity
1	Though the stereotypical "tribe" certainly still exists, modern tribes can be far more than villagers in a far-off land. You've experienced tribes, whether you realize it or not. You know what a "jock" is, right? Or a punk? A surfer? A gear-head? A biker? Describe one of them here. What does he or she look like? What does he wear? Who does he hang out with? What is the essence of the person that causes him to fit within the parameters of the label you have given him? You can even draw a picture of him if you'd like:

Cliques

In high school, we called them "cliques." They were the groups that naturally formed as people grew up together. Jocks, preps, geeks, punks, cowboys, surfers, and band nerds were all grouped according to something that made them like one another and different than others. Every clique on campus had their own particular place on campus at lunch, and each group had its own particular hangouts, style, and language.

#	Questions
1	What clique(s) were you a part of growing up?
2	What were the rules for belonging (what made you a part of the particular group)?
3	In what ways did you have to "work" to remain in good standing (what kept you "in"/what would you have to do to be "out)?"

We Called Them "Cliques ..."

Missiologists call them "tribes." And they are everywhere. People are social beings, and our social circles provide us with a sense of identity. Apart from these social circles, we tend to lose our sense of who we are.

Perhaps the single most significant observation in missions today is this: People everywhere are tribal. Again, for most of us, the word "tribe" brings to mind a primitive group of hunters and gatherers living in thatched-roof huts. In this sense, a tribe is a clan, a sort of extended family that a person is born into.

Rather than being organized around family, modern tribes are voluntary and tend to be based on affinity. People select their social circles, however subconsciously, to replace the clans they were born into while serving the same functions. These are our new tribes.

#	Homework due:__________
1	Describe a tribe you belong to now (stay-at-home moms, mountain bikers, lawyers, etc.). Think about how that tribe shapes and defines you. How do you identify yourself in terms of that tribe? How does the tribe shape you? What would change about you if you could no longer identify with your tribe?

#	Homework, cont.
2	Think about your immediate family and a group of close friends. Make a list of all of the tribes you can identify from their social circles. Consider what it would take for you to join their tribes.
3	**Pray** for each of the tribes that you just identified. Pray for friends who are Christ followers and are already in those tribes that they would be good ambassadors among those people. Pray for the tribes without any Christian presence, that God would send believers to take the gospel to those tribes.

Week Eight: day 2

Modern Tribes

No matter the context, tribes are the social circles we move in. A tribe is the primary social unit to which a person may belong. A tribe has rules, structure, leadership, and goals. Modern tribes may range in connectedness from tightly to loosely knit, and people respond differently to each. Tribes are complex structures, and they give people a sense of identity—who they are and who they are not. People are defined by the company they keep. In his book, *Tribes*, Seth Godin explains that a tribe is any group of people who are connected to one another, a leader, and an idea.[54] Such a definition means that any number of groups are actually tribes, from Apple product users to the Massai of Kenya to high school cliques to the Catholic Church.

All tribes have **common characteristics:**

1. A clear definition of who is "in" and who is "out"—this is the basic parameters of the tribe. It defines the group.
2. Cost of entry/rite of passage—could be as simple as buying a Mac product, more complex hazing into a sorority, or years of Special Forces training.
3. A set of rules and members who enforce them—these rules could be spoken or unspoken, so they may be difficult for an outsider to learn.
4. Consequences for those who break the rules—this could be a simple reprimand, suspension of privileges, excommunication, or worse.
5. An insider language—this could be an actual tribal language, a manner of speaking (sarcasm), or specific catch-phrases that have deep intrinsic meaning.
6. Uniforms—Physical appearance is a social cue that helps people express tribal identity. Difference in uniform within a tribe may denote status to the insider.
7. Leadership—formal or informal, leadership is necessary. Leadership could come from a single person, a group, or even someone behind the scenes (maybe someone the tribe members don't know, i.e. the Pope, Rush Limbaugh, or an influential blogger). Either way, leadership is a necessity.

---

54 Seth Godin, Tribes: We Need You To Lead Us (New York: Portfolio, 2008), 1.

#	Questions
1	For a tribe of which you consider yourself a part, can you define the seven characteristics above? Write them out here (i.e. what is the rite of passage, what is the language, etc.):
2	What implications do these characteristics have on your ability to take the gospel to people around you? What would it take for you to "join" another tribe in order to take the gospel to them?
3	How should this affect the local/global engagement of your local church? Are you taking tribes into account already? What would change if you did?

The Search to Belong

In his 2003 book, *The Search to Belong*, Joseph Myers outlined four major levels of belonging that all people seek—public, social, personal, and intimate.[55] These spaces, as Myers calls them, meet key needs in our lives. The public space is an open and broad social affiliation like being a fan of a particular sports team or driving a certain model of car. The social space fills a more specific need for meaningful interaction, such as one might have gotten in times past from talking to neighbors while sitting on the front porch. Myers' concept of personal space is where the private interaction occurs—things like sharing personal problems or asking for advice. The last space, the intimate, says Myers, is reserved for one or two people with whom we have uninhibited, completely open and honest relationships.

The four spaces are a great way to understand the tribes from a missiological perspective. At one time, all four spaces were filled by family. Today, people choose their communities to meet their needs. To say that people "choose" their community is not to say they are happy with the community they have. Sometimes, people become stuck in a social circle that doesn't meet their needs. This is the problem with most existing social structures; they fail to live up to the needs and expectations of their members.

Furthermore, to say that people select their tribes based on affinity doesn't mean they are any less influential than clan-based tribes. Actually, these chosen social circles often have more influence on the individual simply because the act of choosing them reflects on the one doing the choosing. A person doesn't have any say in what family he's born into, but selecting a social group and going to the trouble of joining it means having much more invested in the resulting connections.

#	**Homework** due:__________
1	Consider your social circles, the groups and activities you are involved in, and others you would like to be. List them here:

55 Joseph Myers, *The Search to Belong* (Grand Rapids: Youth Specialties, 2003), 20.

#	Homework, cont.
2	Go back through the list and mark through any that are faith-based, like church small groups, Christian book clubs, etc. (not that those cannot be missionally focused, but they tend to be filled with people who are already following Jesus). What remains that you are already involved in (hobby clubs, children's sports teams, community/civic groups, etc.) are the tribes in which you already have influence as an insider. Understanding the common characteristics of tribes, how can you leverage that influence for the gospel as an ambassador of God's kingdom? How might this understanding change the way you interact within your tribes?
3	Those remaining on the list that you would like to join are potential spaces for missional activity. What do you need to learn/do in order to join? How does understanding tribes in this fashion change the way that you perceive the opportunities before you to join them?
4	**Pray** for each of the groups you listed. Pray that you would be a conscientious member of the tribes of which you are already a part; that you would be aware of your influence as an insider and look for gospel opportunities. Pray for creativity and acceptance as you move toward joining a new tribe for the sake of the gospel.

Week Eight: day 3

The Function of a Tribe

Tribes do more than just provide their members with a sense of identity. They help the individual process new information. Every day people are bombarded with information. The tribe serves as a filter through which to process that information. Members may discover something new, such as information about an upcoming event or insight into a social event. Then they bring that new information to the group, sharing what they've learned (thereby informing everyone else) and essentially asking, "What do we believe about this?" The underlying question each member is asking is, "What do I believe about this?" The tribe's response will then determine what the individual does with this newly discovered information.

A good example can be found online. Social media provides users with virtual connections and a constant stream of (mostly trivial) data. Every time someone uploads a link to a particularly clever political cartoon or a video of a cat who has learned to knit, he is basically thinking, "I found this and thought it might be of interest to the tribe." When the tribe likes the link, the user is encouraged to find more such information. But a negative response (or no response at all) from one's peers communicates, "This isn't important to us."

Many missionaries employ a methodology that relies strictly on one-to-one proclamation of the gospel. The thinking, of course, is that a decision to follow Christ is personal and individual. However, as tribally connected people, we are limited in our capacity to process major life decisions on our own. **Tribal people do much of their thinking in community.**

#	Question
1	In what ways does your tribe(s) function as a filter of information? Give specific examples:

#	Questions, cont.
2	How does group processing of information affect the way we approach mission? Is one-on-one the most effective manner of gospel proclamation in a tribal society? Why/why not?

Narrative

Information used to be hard to come by. People relied on newspapers and marketplace gossip for information about the world. With knowledge came power; whoever controlled the flow of information controlled society. When information is scarce, it is valuable.

Times have changed. With the advent of the internet, we moved from a dearth of information to open access to unlimited amounts of information in a relatively short period of time. For the first time in history, information is constant. Through the web, text messages, TV, radio, cell phones, print—we are truly overwhelmed with information.

What people need now isn't more information, but filters to sort through the info they already have access to. Good info versus bad. Helpful versus hurtful. Rather than sort through information on our own, people seek influential narrators who filter through the data and offer a complete perspective.

#	Activity
1	Name some influential narrators in the world. What story are they telling? Who is listening to their narrative? What is the result?
2	Who are your narrators? How do they influence you? What about those in your tribes?

Churches Waiting to Happen

It might be tempting to see tribes as barriers to the spread of the gospel. After all, if every social group has its own narrative and requires a unique approach to incarnation, we clearly don't have enough missionaries to make a difference. But viewed another way, tribes are very good for mission. These are essentially groups that meet regularly, enjoy fellowship, tell stories, counsel, support, serve one another, and through it all provide members with a sense of identity. These characteristics may sound familiar because they are the same sorts of things we'd expect to see in a local church.[56]

Of course, unless the members of the group know Christ and meet together for His glory, a tribe is not a church. Not yet, anyway. But among many tribes, the infrastructure is there, already established, but waiting to be jump-started to life by the Holy Spirit. Most of the "work" of church planting is already done for us—tribes are churches waiting to happen!

How would your church's sending strategy change if, instead of seeing existing social structures as barriers to the spread of the good news, we began to see them as direct lines of communication? Instead of considering every person as an individual, we could consider him a representative of his tribe?

56 The International Mission Board, *Definition of a Church*, January 25, 2005 (Richmond, VA: http://www.imb.org/updates/storyview.aspx?StoryID=3838) As viewed February 2012. "A church meets regularly for worship, prayer, the study of God's word, and fellowship. Members of the church minister to one another's needs, hold each other accountable, and exercise church discipline as needed. Members encourage one another and build each other up in holiness, maturity in Christ, and love."

My Place in this World ...

A narrative is a story that explains a tribe's place in the world; so, it's important to understand the narrative of the people to whom you minister. It's the worldview language they speak, including what is wrong with the world, who their enemies are, and accepted values and priorities. Tribes are formed around these narratives. Here you find the questions that the gospel directly addresses: What binds the people? What motivates them? Who among them is hurting? What spiritual influences are evident?

Think about your tribes. Answer the questions above. How is the gospel "good news" that answers the questions the tribes are asking? **Pray** that you and your local church family would be wise in answering their questions by way of the good news of Jesus and His kingdom.

Week Eight: day 4

Is Extraction Really Necessary?

Extraction, according to missional thinker Alan Hirsch, is a typical method of discipleship that removes a new believer from his existing social surroundings in order to acculturate him into an established church.[57] For example, a missionary shares the gospel indiscriminately within a tribe, and by God's grace, some are saved. This, of course, is a very good thing. But the next step is vital. Most missionaries gather those who have come to faith into a new group and consider it a new church. The missionary then switches from evangelism mode to discipleship mode and begins to teach the group of new believers how to do church. Before long, this group of people needs to be encouraged to go out and make non-Christian friends. Churches hold seminars and training sessions about how to relate to lost people. The result is a synthetic, manufactured, Christian tribe that mimics the world's tribes. We end up with a Christian clique (sub-culture, even) just as closed and exclusive as the other groups.

What if, instead of seeing existing social structures as barriers to the spread of the good news, we began to see them as direct lines of communication? Instead of considering every person as an individual, we could consider them as representatives of a tribe. In this light, the gospel is boldly proclaimed into a social circle, and entire groups are discipled. The gospel is trusted to permeate the tribe's discussion and haunt its members' interactions with one another. The resulting group can then take charge of communicating the good news within the tribe. They can demonstrate for others what life in Christ truly means for people of their kind. Instead of removing new believers from their tribes and indoctrinating them in a different culture, we would allow the gospel to permeate their tribes and cultures through natural avenues already in place.

Granted this process takes far more time than typical extractional discipleship models. Discipleship seems much more efficient in a controlled environment. It may take time for an entire tribe to turn to Christ. It is much simpler to remove the new believer from the current tribe (and there certainly are cases where removing new believers is in order). Discipleship in-place will be slower, and the new believer will need spiritual life support along the way. There is great value, however, in discipling someone in place. New believers learn

---

57 Alan Hirsch and Lance Ford, *Right Here Right Now: Everyday Mission For Everyday People* (Grand Rapids: Baker Books, 2011), 215.

to apply their faith to real life, learn theology in their own language, and develop a missional identity that is sealed into their DNA. When the tribe does come to Christ, they will be equipped for the task of cultural translation of the gospel, because they will have learned and walked it together already.

Selah

Consider your own discipleship process. Was it "extractional" or "in-place?" How did it affect your identity as an ambassador? Did it prepare you for mission? Why or why not? (Note: Certainly the gospel is a call to complete and utter abandonment of life as we know it. But it doesn't mean that we must disconnect from the tribes we were in when the gospel found us. The 12 disciples left everything to follow Jesus, but they followed Him in and around their hometowns in full view of their peers.)

Tribes in the New Testament

#	Activity
1	List a few examples of "tribes" you might see in the New Testament:

Oikos

Modern translations of the Scriptures don't actually use the word "tribes." In the ancient Greek, the word *oikos* is translated household but carries the same meaning as tribe. The Greek concept of household would have meant much more than just the structure, building, or even nuclear family. The household was everyone who pertained to a person's societal group—family, extended family, employees, servants—anyone who shared an interdependent life together.

In his paper, *Oikos Evangelism: The Biblical Pattern*, missiologist Thomas A. Wolf wrote about the importance of the tribe to first-century thinking: "An oikos was the fundamental and natural unit of society, and consisted of one's sphere of influence—his family, friends, and associates. And equally important, the early church spread through *oikoses*—circles of influence and association."[58]

The word oikos is mentioned so often in the Scriptures that we can see a pattern; not only individuals repenting and following Jesus, but entire households. It's not entirely clear how this happened. Perhaps the leader of each oikos held such influence that the rest of the members naturally followed suit and converted. Or maybe it was the power of seeing one of their own respond so radically to Christ. The fact that Paul was willing to baptize the various members of each oikos makes it clear that the belief of the tribe was simultaneous and genuine.

#	Scripture
1	All Christians are outsiders to non-believing tribes. Having been sent by the most High God, we go as "ambassadors" (2 Corinthians 5:20) of Christ, citizens of the "household of God" (Ephesians 2:19) to live among people who are "alienated and hostile" to Him (Colossians 1:21). Even the Christian who ministers among the same social group for years can never have complete fellowship with unbelievers (2 Corinthians 6:14). For this reason, the missionary always considers himself to be observing, joining, and influencing from the outside.

58 Thomas A. Wolf, *Oikos Evangelism: The Biblical Pattern* (Golden Gate Baptist Theological Seminary white paper, 1999).

#	Question
1	With that in mind, should we, as missionaries at home or abroad, try to join a tribe in order to influence it, create a new one altogether, or can we remain outsiders, preach the gospel, and expect to see tribes come to faith? What is the default methodology for you and your church?

Our Example

Our model, of course, is Christ Himself, who "emptied Himself, by taking the form of a servant, being born in the likeness of men, being found in the likeness of men. And being found in human form, He humbled himself by becoming obedient to the point of death" (Philippians 2:5-8). The incarnation of the Son is the highest example of mission—the deliberate crossing of cultural boundaries in order to translate the gospel into the context of others. Incarnation means putting oneself in the shoes of another in order that the gospel might be communicated.[59]

59 For a better explanation of incarnational living, see Michael Frost, *Exiles: Living Missionally in a Post-Christian Culture* (Grand Rapids: Baker, 2006), 54-56.

#	Homework	due:__________
1	**Homework** Read the following passages and look for "tribal" language. **Pray** for wisdom as you read, and take time to think about your own opportunities to see entire tribes begin to follow Jesus. Think about where these "churches waiting to happen" may be in your own circles. Luke 19:1-9 - Zaccheus Luke 5:27-31 - Levi Acts 10-11 - Peter and Cornelius What others can you find in the New Testament?	

Week Eight: day 5

It's Hard and Deferential Work

Joining a tribe can be very difficult and take a long time. It requires you to be a student of culture and to deliberately expose yourself to those things who influence the tribe. In order to embed yourself in an oikos, you must leave your preferences and comforts, and, to a certain extent, leave behind much of your cultural identity. It means deliberately changing your lifestyle in order to identify with others. To join a tribe, you must read the books, watch the films, and wear the clothes that shape the tribe.

Even so, despite your best efforts to join a tribe, you will likely never truly be considered a full member of a tribe. At best, you can hope to be considered an "acceptable outsider."[60]

#	Question
1	With that in mind, should we, as missionaries at home or abroad, try to join a tribe in order to influence it, create a new one altogether, or can we remain outsiders, preach the gospel, and expect to see tribes come to faith? What is the default methodology for you and your church?

60 This term was used by Donald Larson in his 1984 book, *Guidelines for Barefoot Language Learning*. Here, we apply the term to even those Christians operating in same-and near-cultures.

When You Don't Fit In

There are cases in which a missionary may not be able to join a tribe for gospel purposes. Can you think of any examples?

When faced with such a situation, there are other options for affecting the tribe for the sake of the gospel.

Focus on group building among those who are socially disconnected

It's human nature to be part of community, and our experience is that not everyone has an oikos; foreigners, outsiders, and new arrivals to a city can be quite disconnected. The missionary can focus on building community among those who are not yet connected.

Shadow pastoring

Another option is to indirectly lead a tribe through "shadow-pastoring." This means positioning yourself to constantly influence by teaching individual tribe members "This is what the Bible says," and then encouraging them to ask one another, "How does that look in our tribal context?" The idea is that the missionary never holds any sort of authority over the group and may never even meet with the group as a whole. Instead, he deliberately remains in the background, teaching, challenging, warning, and encouraging the group toward Christ.

Can you identify places where either of these approaches could be employed in your own life and ministry? In the ministry of your church?

How to Identify Tribes

Identifying the tribes among a people or city requires observation and personal interaction. It is helpful to observe in terms of the four spaces of belonging (recall from Day 2)—public, social, personal, intimate.

Public space tribes tend to be expressed openly. Membership to these tribes usually has a low barrier to entry and provides only a superficial, yet important, level of social connectivity. Think "fans" or "supporters" (sports teams, product users, activists).

Social space connections tend to have more specific meaning for a person's tribal identity. Members connect out of a sense of who they want to be and how they want to be regarded by peers. Think "identifiers" (neighborhood, style of dress, consumer habits, job fields, social activities).

The relationship in the **personal** space is the modern-day equivalent to the social tribe. Here, people process new information, develop their worldview, and seek to be community for one another. Think "primary interaction throughout the week" (small group of close friends, extended family, regular contacts through social media).

The **intimate** space is filled by only one or two people and can be very difficult to identify. These connections have the strongest influence over major life decisions. Think "household" in a stricter sense (spouse, partner, best friend).

Identify these tribes in your own life:

Identify them in the life of someone who is not a Christian with whom you are currently in relationship:

How to Join a Tribe

There is a method to the madness when you are trying to join a new tribe. A missionary has to know what makes a certain group a tribe. What are the distinct characteristics of the tribe that make it, well, a tribe? Here are a few helpful steps to take in identifying them:

Study the Influences

Expose yourself to whatever influences the tribe; it is research through immersion. Read books, watch films, listen to music, and learn from the same news sources. The goal is to begin to understand why the tribe thinks like it does. But don't go alone, and have your guard up. Beware the harmful, and oftentimes subliminal, effects of things like music, film, and story. Nevertheless, go boldly into the tribes, as you are sent by the Most High God!

Adopt the Rhythm

In order to live out the gospel in word and deed among a particular group of people, you must do all that you can to live as they live. We do this by adopting their life "rhythms." (Note that there is a clear distinction between *rhythm* and *lifestyle*. The lifestyle of non-believers is not Christ-centered. Reject ungodliness, but adopt the customs of the group so that they see an example of how their lives might look in Christ.)

- Diet and mealtimes
- Sleeping schedule
- Work hours, rest hours
- Vacation
- Holidays, festivals, celebrations
- Pace of living, busyness
- Social postures, signs of respect
- Economic identification

Learn the Narrative

Immersing yourself in a tribal culture and adopting its rhythms will help you piece together the narrative of the people. You will learn who they are, what they do, and why. You will discover bridges and barriers to the gospel and begin to understand just how the gospel is good news to the tribe.

#	Homework due:__________
1	Identify and consider a "tribe" in your own circles, preferably one that would fall into the public or personal spaces. Write out below what you know about the tribe. What are the influences? Who are the leaders? How do they lead? What are the rhythms of the tribe? How would the members define themselves? Are there obvious bridges and/or barriers to the gospel?
2	What would it take for you to join/influence that tribe for the sake of the gospel? How would you approach them in light of what you know?
3	**Pray** for the tribe. Ask the Lord to send someone into the group with the good news. Ask the Lord if that person is you or another person in your local church body. Pray that God would reveal Himself to the members of that tribe and that they would be drawn to salvation.

Week Eight: Questions for Group Discussion

#	Questions
1	What is a tribe? Share with one another about tribes you are/ have been involved in.
2	Are tribes important to mission? Why or why not?
3	What happens if tribes are not considered in mission? Give a few possible outcomes.

#	Questions, cont.
4	Can a missionary make tribes too important in his approach to a culture? What would be the possible outcomes of over-emphasizing tribes?
5	On Day 2, we discussed seven common characteristics of tribes. Are they universal? Can you give examples of a tribe that may not have all seven characteristics? Are there other common characteristics not mentioned?
6	Does your local church currently consider tribal influence in mission? How so? If not, how would local ministry change if you did? What would it take for your local ministries to begin to work among tribes?

#	Questions, cont.
7	Name and discuss the three marks of the person of peace.
8	How are tribes "filters" of the information that pervades the lives of its people? How does this affect the way people in a tribe process the good news? How should that affect the way missionaries share the gospel?
9	What is the difference between "extractional" and "in-place" discipleship? Are the differences notable? How can extractional discipleship be a hindrance to developing new believers into functional missionaries? What are the inherent dangers in "in-place" discipleship? How can those dangers be guarded against? Name a few instances in which extraction is a necessity. Discuss your own experiences with discipleship. Were you well-prepared for joining Jesus on mission because of it?

#	Questions, cont.
10	Discuss oikos as it is found in the New Testament, citing specific examples. Are the examples in Scripture evidence of coincidence or a particular strategy for mission?
11	Spend some time together in prayer for the specific tribes you pinpointed this week. Talk about these tribes and ask yourselves if the people to take the gospel to them are in the room with you. Talk about what it might take for you to begin to join and/or influence them. Dream, plot, plan, and pray for God to lead you to the tribes He has sent you to influence.

Week Nine: day 1

Contextualization

Say What?

> Si do ta thërrasin, pra, atë, të cilit nuk i besuan? Dhe si do të besojnë tek ai për të cilin nuk kanë dëgjuar? Dhe si do të dëgjojnë, kur s'ka kush predikon? Dhe si do të predikojnë pa qenë dërguar? Siç është shkruar: "Sa të bukura janë këmbët e atyre që shpallin paqen, që shpallin lajme të mira!."[61]

Unless you are fluent in Albanian, the above text probably means nothing to you. Unfortunately, the above paragraph happens to be a message intended for you (Romans 10:14-15). There is a problem. The message has now been delivered to you, but one thing is still missing: translation. For you to even begin to understand what it says, it must be put into a language you can understand. Only then can you reasonably be expected to comprehend, consider, and respond to the message.

All communication requires some effort, but most of it is done subconsciously. For example, if you invited your neighbors to a cookout, you would have to think about the best method to communicate that message. Do you call? Send an email? Ask face-to-face? And you would have to choose the right wording for it to clarify its meaning (include time, place, what the event is, etc.).

However, you are not done there. There are many steps assumed in the process, of which you may not even be aware.

---

61 Albanian translation of Romans 10:14-15. Romakëve 10 (Albanian Bible) http://biblegateway.com.

#	Activity
1	**Activity** Imagine you were inviting your neighbors to a cookout. What unspoken decisions do you make during the process? Make a list here:
2	Did you consider your dress when you visit your neighbors (do you wear pajamas)? What about the time you visit to invite them (is midnight OK)? How loudly would you speak (angrily shout)? If you sent an email, would you send one to everyone? Send it to yourself and bcc everyone? Send a personalized message to each individual? When you really think about it, a lot goes into communicating even the simplest of messages.

Cultural Translation

The more important the message, the more deliberate we want to be in our communication of it. Communicating an important message across cultural barriers requires that we give thought to each step in the process.

Contextualization is the translation of the gospel from one culture to another. More than just converting the good news into an appropriate language for our audience, mission requires that we interpret the message of the kingdom into other cultures through word and deed. Missiologist Charles R. Taber gives this definition:

> *Contextualization* is the effort to understand and take seriously the specific context of each human group and person on its own terms and in all its dimensions—cultural, religious, social, political, economic—and to discern what the Gospel says to people in that context.[62]

For the sake of mission, contextualization means adjusting how we communicate the gospel so that people do not need to join a new culture in order to hear and understand the message. Hence, Jesus' command was to make disciples, not "first-century, Greek-speaking, Roman-ruled Jews" of all nations; and Paul was careful to become "all things to all people" that some might be saved. Our mission is not to export a culture, but to infect existing cultures with what always proves to be a radically counter-cultural gospel.

Wouldn't It Be Easier to De-contextualize?

There are those who would argue that the solution to cross-cultural communication of the gospel is to cleanse it somehow of all cultural bias and distill it to some pure, acultural form. The problem is that such a form does not exist. Gospel events did not occur outside of culture, nor can they be interpreted outside of culture. Christ entered into culture in order to demonstrate God's love and provision for humanity. We call this incarnation: putting flesh on the message. As Christ's body, we too are to act incarnationally; that is, we are to "put flesh" on the good news within the cultural context of the people to whom we are sent. Missiologist David Bosch insisted that "If we take the incarnation seriously, the Word has to become flesh in every new context."[63]

God is glorified by a diversity of human culture. It is He who created the many cultures and dispersed them (Genesis 11, 12), and it is He who will bring them together again to worship around His throne (Revelation 7:9). Contextualization—putting flesh on the good news of Jesus—is our part in the redemption of humanity through the cultures He created.

---

62 Taber, *Contextualization*, 146.

63 David J. Bosch, Transforming Mission (New York: Orbis Books, 1991), 21.

#	Homework due:__________
1	Imagine now that you are delivering a more important message to your neighbors than news of a cookout. You are showing and telling them the good news of the gospel. What are the cultural considerations involved in doing so, both conscious and sub-conscious? List as many considerations as you can that would be involved in one single conversation with a neighbor about the gospel?
2	Now try it again with a neighbor that is culturally different than you, if you did not before (i.e. different ethnicity, different sub-cultural behaviors, etc.).
3	**Pray** for the wisdom to perceive even the minutia of the cultures around you. Read through Genesis 11 and 12 and Revelation 7 prayerfully, and ask God to help you see the beauty of diverse cultures in the same way He does. See and hear His heart for all nations. Pray that you and your church would share His heart for the nations and play your part in incarnating His story of redemption among them—both in your neighborhood and around the globe.

Week Nine: day 2

The Contextualization Debate

While contextualization is indeed basic missiology, it has been the topic of passionate debate in missions for generations. Virtually no one argues that we should not contextualize at all, but there is great debate about the extent to which we should adapt to individual customs and cultures. Some assert that contextualization can easily become a distraction from the bold proclamation of the gospel. Others argue that contextualization should be central to mission, that our job as ambassadors of Christ to the nations is to overcome every cultural barrier to the gospel.[64]

But this is not merely an academic debate; it has far-reaching implications for all people engaging in missions. Those who do not prioritize contextualization spend less time learning languages and adopting local customs. Whereas those who do prioritize it usually begin by doing lots of research and building relationships with nationals.

#	Question
1	Recall your homework from Day 1 regarding sharing the gospel with your neighbor. How might your approach differ if contextualization is a priority for you versus if it is not? If your answers yesterday represent good contextualization, what would your approach be if you are not concerned with contextualization? Which do you honestly believe would be most effective? Why?

64 See for example: http://churchplantingnovice.wordpress.com/2008/03/06/macarthur-on-contextualization/.

For sake of clarity: contextualization is not an attempt to "water down" the gospel to make it more palatable for the hearers. The gospel is offensive enough on its own. Contextualization's goal is removing external walls and offenses that may muddy the waters of the gospel. Contextualization is for the sake of clarity. Our message, the call to repentance and obedience to the Lord Jesus Christ remains the same. Our communication of the message, however, requires creativity, understanding, and effort on our part.

Fortunately, the power of the gospel is not dependent upon our presentation of it. Though some think of contextualization as the pursuit of the perfect way to present the gospel. But there is no single "correct way" to present the good news. We likely will fumble our presentation of the gospel along the way; but our love, patience, and presence will point to our perfectly loving Creator who speaks their language and meets them right where they are.

#	Scripture
In the Gospels, we read of Jesus' use of contextualization of His own story. By contextualizing the gospel, Jesus wasn't making it easier for people to follow Him, but He was making it easier for them to understand the cost. Read the following three stories and think about the audience to whom Jesus was speaking. How did He shape His conversations about the unchanging gospel to fit each particular audience? Below each passage, list the audience, any cultural differences Jesus may have considered, and how He addressed those differences in each case:	
1	Matthew 13:34-43—the crowd versus the disciples

#	Scripture, cont.
2	John 3:1-15—Nicodemus
3	Mark 10:17-27—Rich Young Ruler

#	Homework due:__________
1	In your own words, define contextualization. Why is it important for anyone engaging in mission? Can you think of examples of contextualization in your life or others you know?
2	As you consider again the passages above, **pray** that God would open your eyes, both physically and spiritually, to the cultures of the people to whom you've been sent. Pray that you would understand them well in order to rightly convey the gospel message in word and deed.

Week Nine: day 3

Over- and Under-contextualization

The conversation around contextualization in the missions arena reveals that we're talking about a matter of degrees; everyone believes in some level of contextualization, but to what extent should we contextualize? Fuller Theological Seminary missions professor Dean Gilliland suggests that missionary approaches fall along a continuum of contextualization.

On one extreme lies under-contextualization, in which the message is obscured because not enough is done to ensure the gospel is clearly communicated across cultures. The result is confusion or a complete misunderstanding of the gospel. On the other extreme lies over-contextualization, in which the message is obscured because it sounds so familiar to existing culture that people simply apply a veneer of Christianity to their paganism. This is called syncretism, and it is seen all over the world in cultures who simply apply Christian names to their pagan idols.

Examples

Can you give an example (or several) of under-contextualization of the gospel?

Over-contextualization?

Pick a couple of the examples and describe how each could have been more rightly handled.

Cultural Distance

The goal of contextualization is not to lose the "otherness" of the gospel—the distinct cultural reality and character of God's kingdom. It is simply communicating that gospel faithfully across cultural barriers. Ultimately, the work of the missionary is to contextualize enough that recipients of the message can see, hear, and understand it without having to adopt a foreign culture, but not so much that we lose the uniqueness and exclusivity of the gospel of Jesus Christ. It is the missionary's job to overcome cultural barriers to the communication of the gospel. This will necessarily look different according to unique cultural and sub-cultural contexts. Missiologist Ralph Winter proposed a scale to illustrate the challenges communicating Christ across cultures.[65] It is called the Cultural Distance Scale:

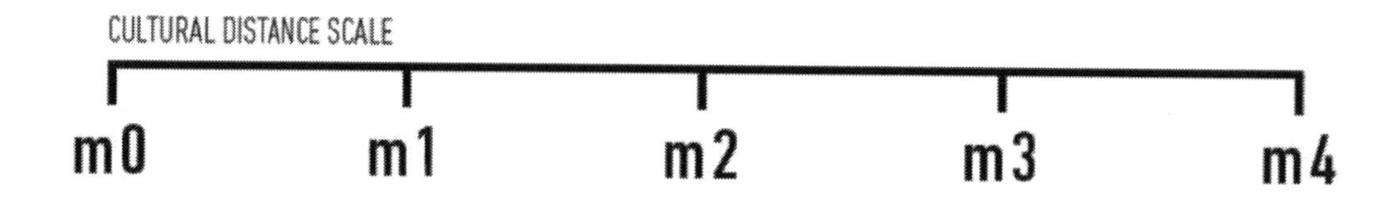

The left side of the scale, m0, represents a believer sharing the gospel with someone who completely shares his or her culture and worldview, such as a sibling, neighbor, or close friend. This is the purest form of evangelism, in that a Christian can share the gospel in much the same way as he received it.

Moving along the scale to the right, we see significant cultural barriers to the communication of the good news. These would be things like language, cultural mores, deeply held prejudices,

65 Winter, "The Highest Priority: Cross-Cultural Evangelism."

idolatry, and the like. Each significant barrier moves us further down the scale, increasing the cultural distance from the missionary to his audience. Greater cultural distance requires greater degrees of contextualization.

Lottie Moon, missionary to the Chinese in the late 1800s, was considered radical in her efforts to contextualize. She was known for dressing and eating like the community to whom she was sent, even though the fare often made her sick. She recognized that her efforts reduced the cultural difference between her and the Chinese, and she gladly gave up her comforts that some might be saved.

When we don't contextualize, we end up exporting our culture and methodologies rather than the gospel of the kingdom. It is why Christianity around the world has taken on an "American" feel, and on any given Sunday you can walk into villages and cities around the world and find churches that look just like those of the American South in the 1950s. Without contextualization, we spread a gospel of "Christ-plus-our-culture" which, of course, is a false gospel.

#	**Homework** due:__________
1	Google search "churches" in an Asian city (Taipei, Hong Kong, Bangkok, Ho Chi Minh, etc.). Click through the resulting websites. Look for churches whose gatherings are in the heart languages of the people there. Look for those who worship corporately in English. Look through the pictures. What is familiar to you as a part of the American church? What do the buildings look like? The setup for corporate worship?

#	Homework, cont.
2	What songs are they singing? What are they teaching? Where do these things originate?
3	What is unfamiliar to you? Are there things in these churches that are distinct to the area?
4	Do you feel as though you could plug into one of the many churches in any of these cities without much adjustment (maybe part of the service is in another language)?

#	Homework, cont.
5	Would you say that these churches are a result of good contextualization, or are they more-or-less transplanted American churches? Would you say that these are expressions of Christ's church unique to the cultures in which they are found? Why or why not?
6	Take an honest look at these churches again. Would indigenous people in these cities have to adopt another culture in order to hear and understand the gospel? Explain.

#	Homework, cont.
7	**Scripture** Read 1 Corinthians 9:19-23. Rewrite it in your own terms, in your own context, as if you were writing to your own church. How might you express his ideas?
8	**Pray** that God would give you a heart after Christ, who wrapped Himself in flesh for the good of a particular people. Pray that you would understand, as Paul and Lottie Moon did, that cultural comforts fade in light of the surpassing riches of knowing Christ. Pray that you and your church would be careful to know the people to whom you've been sent and would do all that you can to remove barriers to their ability to hear and understand the gospel of Jesus Christ.

Week Nine: day 4

Contextualize for Whom?

Contextualization doesn't begin with the missionary, but with the audience; not with statistics and assumptions, but in relationship with real flesh-and-blood people.

A few years ago, a young missionary church planter was sent by his church to work among a people group in North Africa who, statistics told him, were 99.9 percent Muslim. So he set out to study Islam by studying the Quran and Islamic history in order to build cultural bridges to the people. As he began to engage young men in the city in spiritual conversations, the young man realized something about the people: they were only nominally Muslim. In order to stick to his plan for contextualization, he found himself actually teaching the young men what they were supposed to believe as Muslims in order to argue his case for faith in Christ.

Had the young missionary been listening to the stories of his North African neighbors, he would have learned that the oppressed minority needed to hear about freedom in Christ and about His faithfulness. He would have heard their cry for justice, peace, and identity, all of which are found in Christ. Instead, he contextualized for a people that existed only in the statistics at the expense of the people in his community.

#	Questions
1	The young missionary made the classic mistake of acting on stereotypes and numbers on a page, instead of knowing and loving people. Do you recall a time you bought into a stereotype and later learned your assumptions were wrong?

#	Question, cont.
2	What should you have done differently in order to avoid the mistake of wrongly assuming you knew who the person was? How can you avoid the mistake in the future?

More Than Verbal Communication

Contextualization requires the missionary to find the most basic social unit—the largest grouping of people with no internal barriers to the gospel. This could be an ethnolinguistic people group, population segment, clan, village, or urban tribe. Contextualization means considering the language, identity, and culture of the group and adjusting our presentation of the gospel to clearly communicate how it is good news.

Contextualization is more than verbal communication, though. The missionary must consider how his actions may communicate or contradict his message. Denial of self may look different from culture to culture, as may stewardship, blessing, or personal holiness. This is why contextualization is necessary as we proclaim the gospel in both word and deed, that others would see our good works and glorify God (1 Peter 2:11-12).

A college student was sent by her church as a semester missionary to Spain. She was readily accepted by some young Spanish women into their social group. She was invited to dinner, a bar, and then a discoteca. Having never been to a bar or club, she was nervous, but she recognized the rare opportunity to spend so much time with Spanish women in their normal environment. She happily went along and was able to boldly share her faith, pray with the girls, and call them to repentance and life in Christ.

The following day, she called home, excited to share the news with her family back in Texas. To her dismay, instead of celebrating the opportunity she had to share the gospel, her family was appalled that she had visited a bar. "You've ruined your witness!" lamented her mother. The student apologized and never hung out with the Spanish girls again.

Remember, what looks like holiness in one culture may not in another. Had the mother realized that a discoteca in Spain is not like a seedy Dallas bar, but instead a center of Spanish social activity, she may (and should) have celebrated her daughter's incarnational witness among Spanish students. Her failure to contextualize ended her daughter's opportunity to continue to lead Spanish students to follow Jesus.

#	Questions
1	Can you think of examples in your own life when you have failed to contextualize your actions, which may have led to missed opportunities to share the gospel?
2	How might you have handled those situations differently?

#	Homework due:_________
1	Think of a group of people to whom you would like to take the gospel, whether it be a tribe in Southeast Asia, a neighborhood of immigrants in your city, or an urban tribe in your community. The one caveat is that you need to know someone within that group. Make a list of assumptions or stereotypes that people have about them (their likes, dislikes, mores, values, dress, language, etc.):
2	From the relationship you have with the person/people you know in that group, how can you see that they might actually differ from the stereotypes? If you are not sure, what steps can you take to learn?

#	Homework, cont.
3	Can you name an activity (or more) that is a norm in their culture that may be considered taboo in a Christian sub-culture? Is the activity sinful according to Scripture? How will you handle that issue as you take the gospel to them?
4	**Scripture** Read Mark 2:13-17. Consider the people with whom Jesus was eating. For Him to do so was a major "no-no" for good Jews, hence the scowls of the Pharisees. But Jesus ate with them anyway. Explain why. How would Jesus justify breaking one of His cultural mores for the sake of these relationships?
5	Contextualization can be tricky. As we have seen, it can be both over- and under-used. **Pray** for wisdom (James 1:5). Pray that you and your church would exercise the mind of Christ in you (Philippians 2:5-8). Pray that God would give you spiritual insight into the people to whom He has sent you and would go before you to break down cultural barriers to the good news of Jesus.

Week Nine: day 5

Christians Are Outsiders

International missionaries sometimes have it easier than ministers and church planters in their home cultures. When you are clearly an outsider, you act like a guest. You assume nothing; you can't afford assumptions about what people believe or if they understand what you are trying to say. Assumptions can be costly and dangerous, so outsiders are careful about how they communicate.

It is important, then, that all Christians everywhere recognize that they are necessarily outsiders—even those who were born and raised in the same communities in which they minister today. Our citizenship as believers has been moved from earthly kingdoms to the kingdom of God (Philippians 3:20; Ephesians 2:19). Peter implores believers, "as sojourners and exiles," to abstain from sin that discredits our testimony (1 Peter 2:11). As outsiders, we follow Christ's example and incarnate the gospel among those to whom we've been sent.

Even the best of contextualization, however, can only yield limited results. A missionary may live in India, dress and eat like an Indian, and speak fluent Hindi, but he will never be an actual Indian. The most we can expect to become is an "acceptable outsider." However, we can work to minimize the differences between ourselves and those around us in order to proclaim and incarnate the gospel with clarity.

The goal of contextualization is the communication of the gospel that will result in disciples being made and organized into reproducible, indigenous churches. We do this because our Lord modeled this behavior for us, and then commanded us to do the same. He is glorified in diversity as His gospel brings life to every tribe, tongue, and nation.

#	Questions
1	Is it true? Are all Christians outsiders? Explain how so in your own words.

#	Question, cont.
2	How are you an outsider to your particular culture? Make a list below:
3	Does (should) being an outsider affect your daily interactions with others in your workplace, shopping malls, parks, etc.? How?

How to Contextualize:

As we've mentioned already, contextualization begins with culture, with knowing the people in a culture. The best way to learn about a culture is through immersion. In order to understand a people, you must live among them.

1. **Learn the culture**

A key part of culture is **language.** In cases where you're working among people who speak an entirely different language from yours, you must devote the time and effort into learning the grammar, accent, and use of the local language. But even when you're working among people who seem to speak your language, you've got to be mindful of the way people talk.

In your context, is there a difference between how people talk about serious things versus how they talk about the mundane? How so?

Do the words you would normally use to communicate the gospel already have other meanings or negative connotations?

2. **Make a map**

Culture learning cannot be done from an office chair in front of a computer. It takes more than a Google search to understand people. Only through personal interaction will they become people, not statistics or projects. Compile the findings of your research, interviews, and experiences as you build relationships among the people. Use this information to find bridges and barriers to the gospel that already exist in the culture.

3. **Proclamation in word and deed**

Constantly ask: "How is the gospel 'good news' to these people?" (Keeping in mind that, as with the rich young ruler, the "good news" may sound very much like bad news.) Remember that people don't see Jesus in you because you don't smoke, drink, etc. Find out what would help them see Jesus in you.

Practice both presence and proclamation—a verbal and behavioral witness. Make it a habit to tell people what the Bible says and ask them what it would look like in their culture. This helps establish the Scriptures, not the missionary, as the authority in practices of faith. It also helps produce indigenous response to the truth of Scripture. In order to do this, you must study Scripture deeply and often, and recognize the cultural biases you bring to the table.

We all carry certain assumptions, are biased, and carry our own cultural baggage. What biases and cultural baggage can you think of that you may need to stay aware of as you cross cultures with the gospel?

As you share the gospel, trust that it is the Holy Spirit who leads them to Christ, and He speaks their language. Allow for "mistakes." God's global mission involves you, but it doesn't depend on you. Never assume that your strategy, your words, or your personality are enough to win people to Christ, because they aren't. Do your best, and pray for salvation to come to the people.

Never stop contextualizing. Culture is dynamic and ever-changing, and so are our missionary strategies. Just when you think you've found a good way to talk about Jesus to a people, they change. Political climates, social movements, and societal trends are constantly in flux. Influences come and go. Your efforts toward contextualization aren't just to a people, but to a people in a specific time and place. Contextualization isn't a task to be finished, but a posture to be assumed. It's our identity.

#	Homework due:__________
1	Simply have conversations with someone who is culturally different than you. Practice listening and learning. Think about what it might take for you to incarnate the gospel to them. What might you have to change? Is there a language to be learned? Attire? Food? Cultural norms? Are there obvious cultural barriers to you and/or the gospel in place?
2	**Pray** that God would make you keenly aware of your role as an outsider, even in your home culture. Ask him to teach you to think as an outsider, to behave like a guest, and assume no authority in the lives of those to whom you've been sent. Ask God to show you cultural barriers even in your own hometown. Ask Him to teach you how to overcome them.

Week Nine: Questions for Group Discussion

#	Questions
1	Define contextualization. Debate the idea for it—half of the group argue against contextualization and half of it for.
2	Is it possible to de-contextualize the gospel, that is, present it free of cultural influence? Why or why not?
3	Talk about the instances of Jesus' gospel conversations discussed on Day 2. Did Jesus, in fact, employ contextualization? Are there other instances in the life and ministry of Jesus in which you can clearly see contextual sensitivity on His part?

#	Questions, cont.
4	Discuss examples of over- and under-contextualization. Brainstorm ways they could have been handled differently.
5	What is the cultural distance scale? Rate a few specific people within your spheres of influence on the scale. Discuss why they are where they are on the scale and how those barriers can be overcome.
6	Share and discuss your rewritings of Paul's admonition in 1 Corinthians 9:19-23. How might you express the same ideas to your church?

#	Questions, cont.
7	How can you avoid assumptive behavior when engaging in mission locally or internationally? How can you be sure to overcome the stereotypes of people and find out who they really are?
8	What does it mean to be an acceptable outsider? How does that flush out in your normal daily rhythms—your neighborhood, workplace, the park, the grocery store, your hobbies, etc.?
9	Discuss the practical steps of contextualization. How can you implement these practical ideas regularly in your churches and in your own lives? Were you able to begin thinking about how to address cultural issues from your conversation with a friend from Day 5? What conclusions have you drawn? How will you begin to practice good contextualization?

Week Ten: day 1

Pursuing Alternative Paths

Tradition

What does it mean to be a "missionary?" There is a definitive traditional understanding of the word: full-time Christian worker. For most, a missionary is someone who raises funds or is underwritten by a missions organization to move internationally and cross cultures for the sake of the gospel.

How do you define "missionary?" Has it changed since you started this study? How so?

The Problem With *Only* Traditional Mission

Jim worked for a large multi-national company when he and his wife, Shelly, felt led to move overseas on mission.[66] Though his company had offices in the city where they were planning to move, Jim chose to join a mission sending agency and leave his old job. During the process, the 30-something couple met with a missionary who encouraged them to consider a transfer with Jim's employer. A transfer would meet financial needs, provide the essential work permit, and provide access to a large number of nationals. Jim and his wife, however, were committed to being "full-time missionaries" so they could devote all of their time and energy to evangelism, discipleship, and church planting. The couple felt that going through a mission agency would enable them to work out the financial details and work permit and that having access to nationals and a credible reason for interacting with them would be something they would overcome.

Six months later, the missionary who had provided counsel encountered this couple again overseas. They had studied the language and were looking for ways to connect with nationals. Finding it more difficult than expected to start relationships with people who were outside of the church, Jim expressed some regret for not having pursued the possibility of a job transfer with his previous company. He shared that working for a company would have given him both a credible, understandable reason for being in the country and a natural way to enter into relationship with others.

Many people would like to be on mission internationally. The majority of these people are not seminary educated. Instead they work in a range of vocations—engineer, pilot, entrepreneur, salesman, accountant, etc. Sadly, it is very rare that they see and pursue opportunities to use their vocation as a way to be a missionary.

As Jim and Shelly experienced, there are four challenges that missionaries typically encounter today. *Credibility* is an issue in many places. A job title of "missionary" is often a strange and foreign idea to those in another country. *Accessibility* can be a challenge for a person with the title of missionary. It can just be difficult to meet new people. The cost of *living* overseas is a prohibitive factor for some. Obtaining the *essential documents* such as a visa or work permit is also becoming increasingly difficult for the professional missionary.

How could using one's vocation for mission help a "missionary" overcome these four challenges?

Identifying the Paths

Being on mission with God is a journey. It is a marathon that we are to "run with endurance" (Hebrews 12:1) and requires that we continue "looking to Jesus, the founder and perfecter of our faith, who for the joy that was set before Him endured the cross, despising the shame, and is seated at the right hand of the throne of God" (12:2). He, not our mode of missional engagement, is the focus. The journey is about our mission with Him. Alternative paths, strategies, approaches, or tactics are a part of our obedience to Him.

There are two broad categories of paths: traditional paths and alternative paths. Both of these categories have multiple expressions—not singular. The reason is that Scripture does not prescribe one definitive way to always do mission. Whether a path is traditional or alternative may be identified by examining four features of the mission effort: identity of the missionary, mode of mission, location of mission, and how God provides the resources for mission.

A summary of these four can be broken down as follows:

	Traditional Paths	Alternative Paths
Identity of the missionary	Missionary or full-time minister	Tentmaker or other creative platform
Mode of mission	Preaching to others	Interacting with others
Location of mission	Worship or evangelistic gathering	Marketplace, homes of non-believers, places where people gather
Resources for mission	Funded through the church	Funded through the market

Not Really Alternative

What we are calling "alternative" paths here are not alternative in that they are out of the norm, at least not biblically. We have labeled them as such because they are different than the traditional approaches common to mainstream modern mission efforts. They are, in fact, "alternative" to the most common full-time Christian worker scenario. In the Bible, however, vocational mission is far from outside the norm.

#	Homework due:__________
1	Think through the New Testament and find examples of "alternative" mission approaches in actions. Look for people working regular jobs, living regular lives among people who did not follow Jesus for the sake of the gospel. Write down a few stories here:
2	The idea of finding alternative paths to mission has actually been rather controversial. There are those who would not count people living and working regular jobs across cultures for the sake of the gospel as real "missionary" work. The Bible just does not agree. Many of the new churches seen in Acts did not come out of the work of the Apostles, but out of the Diaspora—the Christians who had to flee persecution. **Pray** for the church as a whole, that we would embrace again the same missionary identity as those scattered abroad in the early church.

Week Ten: day 2

Two Paths in Action

At the beginning of Acts, we observe Peter using a traditional approach. Unequivocally, this was the leading of the Holy Spirit. On the day of Pentecost, he preached and God-fearing Jews from every nation heard the gospel in their own language and believed. We read that 3,000 were added to their number that day (Acts 2:1-41). Peter was easily identifiable in this story as a preacher, evangelist, or full-time minister. The mode of mission on this occasion was preaching. Through use of this traditional approach, Peter was used by God in accomplishing His mission.

Paul used the same approach, especially during his early missionary journeys. But later in his ministry, he identified himself as a tentmaker. His mode of mission included training other missionaries as well as interacting with other tentmakers—like Aquila and Priscilla—and people in the city (Acts 18:1-4). He moved his meeting location from the temple to the hall of Tyrannus (Acts 19:8-10). His tent making would have continued to keep him among other tentmakers and in the marketplace, as well. God provided Paul with the financial resources he needed to be on mission through his marketplace work. Because of Paul's efforts, "all the residents of Asia heard the word of the Lord, both Jews and Greeks" (Acts 19:10).

It is clear that God used Peter's methodology in Acts 2 and Paul's in Acts 18-19. There is not a right or wrong approach or path to mission here. The methods can even be mixed, as evidenced by Peter ministering in a home (Acts 10) and Paul preaching or teaching in the temple. All four features of a mission effort do not have to fit exclusively in the traditional or alternative path column. Instead, the church needs to realize that an informed, effective, and culturally appropriate sending of her people will include both traditional and alternative paths to mission. A sending church needs to utilize different paths in different contexts, both economic and social, based on the giftedness of the one(s) being sent.

#	Questions
1	Why would Paul have used different approaches? Are there any clues in his writings that might lead us to his motives? If so, how might those motives shape the way we think about sending methodologies?

#	Questions, cont.
2	**Paul's Parting Words to Friends** In these parting words to his missionary disciples, Paul placed special emphasis on his tent making work. It was important to him not to be a burden to the church, but tent making meant something else to him, as well: *I coveted no one's silver or gold apparel. You yourselves know that these hands ministered to my necessities and to those who were with me. In all things I have shown you that by working hard in this way we must help the weak and remember the words of the Lord Jesus, how He himself said, 'It is more blessed to give than to receive.'* (Acts 20:33-35) Paul was excited about the fact that he worked not only to care for his own needs, but also to generate funds that allowed him to be a blessing to those in need. This is actually very telling about what Paul believed to be a very important part of mission, and he pointed back to Jesus to explain it. What do you think this passage has to do with how he approached mission? What was he so excited about? How did it affect mission for him? How should it affect mission for us?

#	Homework due:__________
1	Make a list of any positives you see with using an alternative path for missionary engagement. Go ahead and list the negatives, as well. You will discuss these with your group later.
2	**Pray** through the above passage from Acts 20. Pray that in whatever way possible you and your church may be a blessing to others as you engage in God's mission locally and globally. Pray for insight into what may keep you from being as much of a blessing as you could be and make notes of those things.

Week Ten: day 3

Examining Alternative Paths

Too many Christians view mission as something that can be accomplished only through a traditional approach. If someone wants to go and be on mission, common practice requires that they quit their job, go through extensive training, develop funding avenues, and finally, make the move. But in so many places and niches in the world today, that just does not make sense.

In many of those places, there are professionals, experts, students, and others that are needed to shine the light of Christ. These "missionaries" need to be recognized, honored, trained, and prayed for as what they are—missionaries. Also, in many parts of the world, full-time Christian workers are struggling to find relevance and ways to connect to a lost world. Alternative paths are ways that these various types of missionaries are finding to be on mission in various locations in credible ways.

The number of people being sent out through the churches using alternative paths is small but growing. Sending churches are beginning to consider alternative paths as the number of people seeking to go on mission increases. Often, we have seen families go on mission in this way without their church being aware. The churches need to send these people—on purpose. How they equip and send them out needs to increasingly become a part of their tradecraft.

#	Question
1	Why would Paul have used different approaches? Are there any clues in his writings that might lead us to his motives? If so, how might those motives shape the way we think about sending methodologies?

Types of Paths

There is a seemingly endless number of alternative ways to function as a missionary. Categorizing the possibilities helps spur creativity about possible alternative mission strategies.[67] Three types of alternative paths are: secular, creative, and platform strategies. These are not necessarily mutually exclusive, but most approaches tend to fall primarily into one of these three categories.

Secular paths to mission exist where someone gets a *regular* job or studies like a normal student and uses their new assignment for mission. Common approaches here include taking a job with an existing company, a non-profit organization, or studying as a university or graduate student for academic credit. Because secular paths are not dependent on donor support, they provide one of the easiest ways to start on mission in terms of funding, using existing infrastructure or opportunities to go and make disciples while fulfilling work requirements.

What are a few examples of this type of missionary engagement?

Creative paths to mission are those that exist by starting something new. Options here are unlimited. These may be created to meet the needs of an entity (business-driven), people, or place (mission-driven). Creative paths may take the form of a for-profit or non-profit entity. This category offers an opportunity for a business that is already profitable in a line of products or services to open a branch or division in another place. A business can strategically "out-source" a business function to another place. Options here could include traditional outsourcing with intentionality or maintaining control in-house though moving the office to another place in the world. This occurs when a company locates an aspect of its business like information technology or accounting to another part of the globe. Another creative strategy would include starting a new business or non-profit organization that develops

67 The most widely recognized categorical system of this kind was put forward by Patrick Lai in his book *Tent-making*. It has been an invaluable part of the business as mission conversation. However, to simplify and seek to value approaches a bit differently, I have proposed this new categorization. Patrick Lai, *Tent-making: The Life and Work of Business as Missions* (Colorado Springs: Biblical Publishing, 2005), 21-28.

around a people or place. Creative paths provide one of the greatest opportunities to dream big strategically in order to develop an avenue that significantly advances the gospel.

What are a few examples of this type of missionary engagement?

Platform paths to mission are jobs, roles, or functions that allow professional missionaries to relate to people in culturally appropriate ways. These paths are for missionaries that are already funded through support, a mission agency, or through personal resources. Using a skill, hobby, or profession, a missionary finds a way to interact with the people he is working among. Platform efforts are usually low in capital requirements, which makes them relatively easy to begin and terminate.

What are a few examples of this type of missionary engagement?

#	Homework due:__________
1	Brainstorm about your church. Are there those within your congregation who might fill one of the above roles in mission? Do you? How might your church equip them to do so?
2	**Pray** for creativity for your local church and leadership as you consider equipping your own people for mission through whatever path they may be gifted and equipped to walk.

Week Ten: day 4

Critical Components

One of the challenges with discussions about alternative paths to mission is the vast scope. To date, these conversations have often been referred to as *business as mission* (BAM), *tentmaking*, developing a *platform,* and creative access. While the BAM and tentmaking designations have referred more to a business approach that does mission, platforms and creative access have been the domain of missionaries developing a business entity or approach to help their mission efforts. However, all of these terms can connote different things to different people.

While all of the above can prove helpful, there is one variant that has proved consistently problematic. Half-hearted, undeveloped attempts at pursuing alternative paths to mission do not go well.

After the World Trade Center towers were attacked on September 11, 2001, ramifications were felt around the world. Many of the universities in other countries that missionaries had previously had free access to began to close their campuses. Individuals that were not students or organizations had to apply for access to be there. Some missionaries that had been working with universities simply had business cards printed up to gain access. In some places this worked for a season. In other locations it did not. Over time, some universities became more stringent in checking the reason for being on a campus. I have seen multiple mission organizations lose access to university campuses for going in under one identity and purpose but then doing something else. Since the missionary viewed himself only as a missionary, he did not fulfill the role he had promised. Many have referred to this as a bait and switch tactic. This has led to loss of access to some universities and organization. Additionally, partial attempts have caused some missionaries to be expelled from a country and have their visa be revoked.

Do you know any bait-and-switch stories, whether in local or international mission? Share your story(ies) here:

Five Components

For all types of whole-hearted attempts to being on mission through creative access, there are five key components to consider.[68]

The starting point to doing any type of mission well is to have a *sending church*. The sending church commits to pray for them, remember them, visit them when they are discouraged, and help them in whatever ways are needed. They also learn from each other and hold each other accountable.[69] Whether you are considering going through a mission organization or directly through your church, this is still a key step.

Second, it is important to have a *job*. This is pretty straightforward. Not always easy, but clear enough. Creativity and networking in the job search process is vital for most.[70] For a missionary or mission agency seeking to enter into a place, it may require setting up an entity or credible service that is either a for- or non-profit. Involve some entrepreneurial minds in this process. The job is necessary for income, credibility, and access.

Third, *training* is essential. Those that have not been intentional in mission before are usually anxious to receive input. For any that may have experience in a traditional approach to mission, coaching from others can provide a healthy alternate perspective to identify ways to live missionally among coworkers. Either way, they should be equipped as missionaries that make disciples that make disciples.

Fourth, having a *local ministry connection* is desirable. Where possible, seek to come alongside others that are making disciples, starting groups, and planting churches. This may be a local church. In many locations there will be a missionary or national church planter seeking to advance the gospel. If working together is viable, it can encourage all involved.

Fifth, participating in a community of like-minded people can be critical. There will be times of frustration and discouragement. Even the most laser-focused committed person can lose sight of the objective in the process. The Great Commission is not a lone ranger journey. It is done best in community with encouragement as you share together what God is doing, what you are learning, and lifting each other up in prayer.

---

68 These five key components come from the Skybridge Community. While these are driving factors of Skybridge, these components are not the exclusive domain of Skybridge. Skybridge Community, http://www.skybridgecommunity.com/.

69 Acts 13:1-3; 14:24-28.

70 A good starting place—Richard Nelson Bolles, *What Color is Your Parachute?* http://www.jobhuntersbible.com/.

These are particularly directed at people moving internationally for mission. They are relevant for missionaries in their own local context. How so? How are these components relevant to you, in particular?

Celebrate

If alternative paths to mission are going to be a key part of mission, then some celebratory changes are essential. The church must encourage those that are ready to give their life to the gospel whether as full-time Christian workers, marketplace workers, or some hybrid of the two. Churches should be sending them out with her blessing, training, support, and prayer. Churches should journey along with those they send out to encourage and be encouraged by them. To teach and be taught by them.

Celebrating them can also mean developing ways to equip them. Churches need to train marketplace workers in mission and theology. They cannot quit their jobs in order to go to seminary, but they need training nonetheless. If local churches value marketplace workers in mission, they must develop methods of equipping them for engagement.

#	Homework due:__________
1	How is your church equipping marketplace workers for mission? How are you celebrating them publicly? How are you praying for and supporting them? How might you improve?
2	**Pray** for your church. Pray that you would together faithfully encourage and equip men and women to boldly represent Christ in the workplace both locally and internationally. Pray that you would be creative as you celebrate the unique opportunities they have to live as salt and light in places others could never go.

Week Ten: day 5

Alternative Paths: How-to

Analytical thinking is critical in evaluating alternative paths to mission. They should deal with the issues of credibility, accessibility, cost of living, and essential documents. When deciding whether or not to pursue an alternative path to mission, the missionary, in partnership with the sending church, should answer three key questions.

- Is there an access issue that needs to be overcome? This can range from getting a visa into a country to whether or not the missionary is able to gain access to a specific people. For example, a missionary sent to work with university students in a place where access to the university is restricted could pose a problem. Through an alternate approach, access issues can disappear. Non-religious visas often provide greater access around the world.
- Is developing relationships with people a challenge? Regardless of the reason, if a missionary is unable to develop meaningful relationships with the lost in a culture, making disciples will be an impossible endeavor. Alternate paths that will cause sustained, significant interaction with a people will be helpful.
- Are the people largely non-responsive to the gospel? Sustained interaction with a people can often foster a pre-discipleship process that will lead to people becoming Christ followers.

If the answer to any of these questions is yes, then alternative paths to mission deserve prayer and investigation. Pray continually and at this point in the journey, devote extra time to prayer.

#	Questions
1	Are there or have there been access issues with any missionaries your church has sent out? How did you deal with them? Were they able to be overcome?

#	Questions, cont.
2	Do you know of missionaries who have struggled with developing relationships? Do you think that an alternative path may have given them inroads to relationships they may not have had otherwise?

Strategy

If you arrive at the conclusion that an alternative path is a good next step, you need to evaluate possible strategies. Evaluating these questions as a team will produce better results. The team will benefit by having at least one strategic thinker and cultural expert.

- Does the strategy fit the people and culture? Would the strategy meet the needs of or benefit nationals in some way?
- Does the strategy enable the missionary to both maintain integrity and operate with wisdom? The strategy being considered should position the missionary as one that can transparently be a Christ-following disciple-maker while positioning him to have influence in society.
- Does the strategy allow for close, sustained interaction with non-believing nationals? Some alternate paths just provide access. The optimal approach would be a strategy that develops situations where Christ-centered conversations naturally develop regularly.
- Does the strategy positively impact the goal of missions? Does the job allow time for relationship building (i.e. is it a 60 hour/week job? When do you build relationships)? Also, there is an increase in the number of policies companies maintain that prohibit proselytizing and church planting. This is an issue that needs attention and prayer.

Look Before You Leap

Before committing to move forward, consider these before-you-jump questions:

- Are the sending church and missionary in agreement about an alternative path? This may require a process of vision casting, but a sending church and, if present, the mission agency should be supportive of an effort or the missionary must reconsider the strategy.
- Does the missionary, mission team, or church possess the necessary expertise and resources to make a particular path viable? Without some level of competence, alternative missions end badly. As the ones bearing the name of Christ, we should seek to excel in all areas for the sake of His glory.
- Is the disciple-making process reproducible for a future indigenous movement? Whether or not a particular alternate strategy is reproducible may not be an issue, but it is critical that the process of making disciples not be overly embedded in a strategy.
- Has counsel been sought from others that may be more knowledgeable than I am on the strategy? Take advantage of the wisdom found in the body as a whole.
- Is there a simpler way to meet the goals that we have not tried yet? Any possible traditional path to missions or simpler alternative path should be evaluated as a possibility.

The process of starting well on an alternative path may seem a bit overwhelming. That is probably a good thing to be aware of. However, when working in community with others that are gifted in working through similar processes, the dreaming process can be a lot of fun and may move quicker than you might expect. During the journey, continue to seek the Spirit's leadership. That's essential for any mission endeavor all along the way—from beginning to end.

#	Homework due:__________
1	Simply **pray** for your church. Pray that you would be open to the leadership of the Spirit as He guides you into new and exciting avenues of mission. Pray for wisdom for your church leadership and for men and women who would recognize the importance of exploring alternative paths to mission.

Week Ten: Questions for Group Discussion

#	Questions
1	Discuss your answers to the following questions from Day One: How do you define "missionary?" Has it changed since you started this study? How so?
2	How can alternative paths to mission help a missionary overcome issues with credibility, accessibility, cost of living, and obtaining necessary documents?
3	What are some examples from Scripture of people who pursued alternative paths to mission? What are some examples of modern missionaries who are pursuing alternative paths?

#	Questions, cont.
4	Discuss the question from Day 2 regarding Paul's motives for using multiple approaches to mission. Does he address his motives in Scripture?
5	Your homework on Day 2 included listing the positives and negatives of alternative approaches. Discuss those among the group. Do the positives outweigh the negatives within your group? How can the negatives be overcome?
6	How can you equip people within your local church for marketplace mission? Are you doing anything already? How can you celebrate what is already being done?

#	Question, cont.
7	Are there existing marketplace workers within your church body that may either be prepared to be sent out as marketplace missionaries or can speak into equipping people for marketplace mission?
8	How are you preparing and equipping people to be on mission in their marketplaces locally? How does your church celebrate local marketplace mission?

Week Eleven: day 1

Protecting Indigeneity

#	Activity
1	Quickly describe (or draw) the church building in which you currently gather with your local church, i.e. layout, decor, flow, setup of worship space, etc.
2	Now describe what happens in a typical worship gathering with your local church (everything from dress to musical style to teaching to language spoken):

#	Activity
3	Now imagine you are walking through a squatter's camp just outside a city dump in Brazil or a small African village or even a large city in Asia and you come across what you just described above. Does it fit in any of those places? Would it make sense to take your local expression of church and transport it into any of these other places? Why or why not?

It Happens ... A Lot.

What you've just considered really happens, and it is not an isolated occurrence. There are churches all around the world operating in this exact manner. Imported hymns, architecture, and decorations that mimic American churches, and even English language for public services pervade churches all over the globe. It is not uncommon for the culture of the host country to be completely absent from the worship setting and replaced by mid-century American church culture. Local believers often lack the freedom to explore indigenous (culturally appropriate) expressions of church.

The problem with this type of approach is that churches and missionaries are actually adding a barrier to the gospel by importing culture that has nothing to do with it. By including English language and American church practice in a distinctly non-American setting, the missionary is inadvertently saying that people must become Americans before they can become Christians. Therefore, it is imperative for missionaries to protect indigeneity by properly exegeting the culture and discerning what the church should look like in that context.

#	Question
1	Think about a typical worship service with your church. If you knew that the entire congregation in your next service would be Chinese immigrants, what would you change about the service? What would remain the same?

Indigenous

"Indigenous" is an agricultural term that means "generated from within or capable of originating from within the local context."[71] A plant is indigenous if it originates in the place it is found. The opposite of indigenous is exogenous, which is defined as "originating outside of the local environment; foreign, extraneous in origin."[72] A transplanted species is exogenous. A wooded, country road in eastern Tennessee lined with eastern white pine or silver maple trees is an example of indigenous plant life. Those species are naturally found there. The same road lined with Hawaiian koa trees or any sort of palm tree, plant life not naturally found in the region, boasts exogenous foliage.

71 "Indigenous," Merriam-Webster Online Dictionary, accessed September 11, 2012, http://www.merriam-webster.com/dictionary/indigenous.

72 "Exogenous," Merriam-Webster Online Dictionary, accessed September 11, 2012, http://www.merriam-webster.com/dictionary/exogenous.

Horticulturist Paola Zannini describes North American native, indigenous plants as any that were growing in North America before the European settlement. She points out that the advantages of native plants are obvious. "Native plants, once established, are more adaptable to our gardens, and they contribute to create an ideal habitat for desirable wildlife such as butterflies and birds."[73] In other words, indigenous gardens thrive easier than those made up of their non-indigenous counterparts.

Zannini offers a few important steps on growing native plants. Among others, she suggests that garden habitats should reflect the natural environment from which they come. Once such a habitat is created, care should be given for the plants until they are well established and can withstand extreme weather conditions.[74]

Indigenous churches are fellowships that are native to their local soil where they can grow, thrive, and reproduce. As such, the churches planted need to necessarily reflect the culture in which they are planted. There will be enough work in understanding the depths of sin, grace, and redemption without the added work of learning a new culture. The transmission of the gospel on its own merit will face extreme conditions in any culture, and young believers within that culture will need assistance—discipleship—in understanding how it is counter to parts of their own particular culture.

The most effective way to plant the gospel in a new culture is as free of external cultural influence as possible. Missiologist Ed Stetzer wrote that the task of mission is to transplant the gospel into a new community so that the church could become "native" there.[75] If thriving, reproducing, native churches are the end goal of our work in mission, then we must protect the indigeneity of the churches among those to whom we are called. It is in those native churches that indigenous people will find the comfort and freedom to explore the gospel and the life change that comes with it without the cumbersome weight of learning another culture in order to understand it.

---

73 Paola Zannini, "Five Tips for Growing Native Plants", Times Free Press.com, February 5, 2011, accessed May 15, 2012, http://www.timesfreepress.com/news/2011/feb/05/5-tips-for-growing-native-plants/.,

74 Ibid.

75 Ed Stetzer, "Indigenous Church Planting," Church Planting Village.net, accessed May 15, 2012, http://www.oklahomachurchplanting.com/wp-content/uploads/2012/12/Indigenous- Church-Planting.pdf.

#	Homework due:__________
1	Think about your own home church. What is required of people in order for them to hear and understand the gospel? Are there particular cultural barriers that inhibit the transmission of the gospel in culture around you? Are there tribes around you that might need further culture consideration to understand the gospel? Make a few notes here of your thoughts and **pray** for wisdom to address these issues.

Week Eleven: day 2

In the 15th century, the Spaniards moved into South America bringing with them European colonialism, and the architecture of the buildings they built there reflects just that. Still to this day, a walk through Lima, Peru, will at times feel like a walk through Spain.

People and cultures were present in South America before the Spaniards arrived. Just as in other instances of colonization, the cultures of the indigenous people were written-off as heathen and Spanish culture was deemed Christian. Spanish church buildings were then built, and Spanish Christian evangelization began, ignoring the cultural nuances of the people they were evangelizing.

#	Questions
1	What problems do you see with this approach, if any?
2	Why/how would imported culture be a barrier to the spread of the gospel and the planting of indigenous churches?

Good Intentions

Spanish Catholics weren't the only ones to export their religious culture in the name of mission. Similar examples exist in evangelical missions over the past 50 years. The effects of religious culture exportation are obvious—tribal African preachers who feel they must always wear a coat and tie to preach and developing countries whose people live in huts but worship in church buildings constructed in the form of Southern American architecture. It is not uncommon for churches to simply export their model of church from their current setting into another city and context abroad.

One well-meaning church wanted to help a missionary reach his city by starting a cutting edge church service. The church's strategy was to literally put all they needed, including chairs and sound equipment, into a crate and ship it to Europe. They even offered to translate their pastor's videos into the host language each week to be played at the service. They believed that all the missionary needed to do was find an attractive venue and turn on the DVD player.

No doubt the intentions of the church were good, but they started with a faulty assumption—if it works here, it must be good anywhere. The natural next step in that process of thought was to export their good and useful product. The problem is that there was no consideration given to cultural context, which is always a huge barrier for the gospel.

#	Homework due:__________
1	The problems with exporting culture globally are clear and obvious, but the same issues affect local gospel work, as well. Physical proximity does not equal cultural sameness. Ministry within a certain area of your city defined spatially will not necessarily guarantee a homogenous audience who will respond to the gospel in kind. Even within a relatively small space there can be a mix of cultures that would respond to the gospel differently. Make a list of the ministries you/your church are involved in within your city.

#	Homework, cont.
2	After you have completed your list, go back through the list and underline any of the ministries that have a specific cultural consideration (i.e. ESL classes, worship services in another language, outreach to people of a particular culture or tribe). What steps have you taken to allow for gospel expression within their particular culture (i.e. do you have the Spanish worship service in the same space, with the same decor and music as your English services; or is there freedom for those who are believers in that culture to shape the worship gathering and infuse their culture into their response to the gospel)?
3	How could you improve your efforts to encourage indigenous response that makes room for culture in local expressions of the church and ministry?

#	Homework, cont.
4	In the contextualization section of this workbook, we studied 1 Corinthians 9:19-23 and rewrote it in terms of your own church context. Contextualization has to do with how the unchanging gospel is translated into ever-changing culture. Indigenous churches are the result—churches that express the unchanging gospel through the lens of the culture in which they are planted. From the list above, think through the ministries you underlined that have specific cultural emphasis. If contextualization is involved in carrying out those specific ministries, how might they lead to indigenous churches among those cultures? What is the relationship between contextualization and the planting of indigenous churches?
5	It is God who created cultures, and there is great value in them. In fact, a peek into the throne room of God in Revelation 7 reveals this picture: 9 After this I looked, and behold, a great multitude that no one could number, from every nation, from all tribes and peoples and languages, standing before the throne and before the Lamb, clothed in white robes, with palm branches in their hands, 10 and crying out with a loud voice, "Salvation belongs to our God who sits on the throne, and to the Lamb!" God values cultures, and He desires to be worshipped from within every one of them. The picture of every nation, tribe, and tongue giving honor to God is beautiful. Pray that you and your church would also see great value in other cultures. Pray that you would see people within other cultures around you come to know Christ and churches spring up that express their faith in ways that are biblically faithful and culturally appropriate.

Week Eleven: day 3

Indigenous Churches

British missionary Roland Allan wrote that "an indigenous church, young or old, in the East or in the West, is a church which, rooted in obedience to Christ, spontaneously uses forms of thought and modes of action natural and familiar in its own environment." Missiologist Allen Tippet added his thoughts to the conversation: "When the indigenous people of a community think of the Lord as their own, not a foreign Christ; when they do things as unto the Lord, meeting the cultural needs around them, worshipping in patterns they understand; when their congregations function in participation in a body which is structurally indigenous; then you have an indigenous church."[76]

As we see in these definitions, indigenous churches are simply rooted in the cultural context from which they arise and include thought and action common to the culture within their worship practices. Particularly, Tippet's definition speaks to why indigeneity is even important—it helps people understand Christ as their own Lord, not a foreign God. They see Christ not as the God of people completely different than them, but as who He actually is—the God of all of the diverse peoples of the world.

Therefore, indigenous churches are incredibly important for mission, as well, whether local or international. Indigenous churches live and worship in a manner that the cultures in which they are rooted understand. In short, when indigenous churches are on mission in their own particular culture, they are unhindered by cultural differences and expose the clear difference between people transformed by the gospel and those who are not. The life-changing power of the gospel is unimpeded by cultural barriers.

It's About the Whole Church ...

Being indigenous affects much more than simply the church planter (read: missionary). It is more about the nature of the church as a whole than simply who the church planter is. However, the church planter influences the church much like the horticulturist influences the growth of plants. Consider this North American scenario from Ed Stetzer:

> A church planter [in Chicago] may be from Chicago, but if the church is dependent on offerings from Alabama, has adopted an Alabama style of worship, and meets at the time that the farmers in Bessemer, Alabama set 100 years ago, the church may not be indigenous for Chicago (though

---

76 Ibid.

perhaps it would be in Bessemer). The origin of the church planter is not the determining factor of being indigenous. Instead, the nature of the church plant is. A person from Chicago is more likely to lead an indigenous church because he has been raised in that area. However, if education or other influences are non-indigenous in nature, the church planter might start a church that is out of place in the local culture."[77]

If we follow this idea to its logical conclusion, an indigenous church is the proof of the gospel being incarnated within a certain cultural context. The lack of indigenous expressions and the presence of foreign ones prove a lack of cultural insight and care for the local people. To go to the "all peoples" of the Great Commission, we need to plant the unchanging gospel into new cultural soil and let it take root there.[78]

#	Activity
1	Consider the church planter from Bessemer, Alabama, mentioned above. What protections might he put in place to avoid importing his culture into Chicago?

77 Ibid.

78 Ibid.

#	Activity, cont.
2	Would his efforts require the same sort of protections if he were working among young professional families living in the city of Birmingham, Alabama? Why or why not?

How Do We Protect Indigeneity?

Again, Roland Allen challenged the church to champion indigeneity in his book Missionary Methods—St. Paul's or Ours? He listed five main ways missionaries can protect indigeneity:

- The teachings must be easily understood so that those who listen can retain it, use it, and pass it on.
- Churches and organizations in the new culture should be set up in a way that national Christians can maintain them.
- Church finances should be provided and controlled by the local church members.
- The Christians should be taught to provide pastoral care for each other.
- Missionaries should give national believers the authority to exercise spiritual gifts freely and at once.[79]

Each of these points is written to pertain to international mission, but each applies to local mission, as well. As we studied in the section on tribes, distinct groups of people with particular cultures exist everywhere, making contextualization and indigeneity imperative in both local and global mission.

79 Roland Allen, *Missionary Methods—St. Paul's or Ours?* (Cambridge: Lutterworth Press, 2006), 151.

#	Homework due:__________
1	Rewrite the five principles above in your own words as they pertain to local ministry in your city. Think in terms of the tribes in your city, particularly the ones with which you and your church work.
2	**Pray** for the people to whom God has sent you individually where you live, work, and play. **Pray** for the people to whom God has sent you collectively as a local church both locally and globally. Ask the Lord for wisdom to know and understand the people to whom He has sent you so that you can rightly equip them to develop churches that are appropriate expressions for the cultures from which they come.

Week Eleven: day 4

Behind the five principles we learned yesterday, there are five underlying principles we will explore over the next two days that are key to developing missionary strategy.

Understanding Cultural Context

As we've discussed in the section on contextualization already, understanding the culture is a priority when engaging any cultural context with the gospel. When people must abandon their valued cultural identity and adopt an alien culture in order to become believers, the cause of church planting will not go far. Around the world, many churches that appear culturally out of place in their setting serve as testimonies to this obstacle. In too many instances, church planting has become cultural warfare, as missionaries and local Christians attempt to conquer and change the culture rather than the hearts of the people. Whenever one must become like a Russian, American, European, or any other culture foreign to his own to become a Christian, there is little chance that the movement will spread rapidly among those people.

#	Scripture
1	Acts 15:1—But some men came down from Judea and were teaching the brothers, "Unless you are circumcised according to the custom of Moses, you cannot be saved." What were they saying was a prerequisite for salvation? Was it a biblical position, or a religious/cultural norm? How so?

#	Scripture, cont.
2	How would people outside of the Jewish tradition have been affected if the early church had come to a different conclusion on the issue of circumcision as the gospel spread?

Reproducing Disciples

For decades, Western church planting has been focused, for the most part, on the weekend gathering. Just look at the common metrics—how many people are in your church (answered by the number that attended last Sunday)? How is the band? The message? The kids' space? The parking? The signage? The thematic drama and video? The coffee?

Those things are meant to draw a crowd, which has been our priority. It has been the starting point for every ministry, instead of a celebration of what has been happening throughout the week. As a result, we have focused the majority of our time and resources on making the church gathering experience meaningful, and we have unfortunately short-changed discipleship.

Simply put, we have focused on producing quality church services instead of reproducing disciples. Instead of understanding the culture and needs of the people around us and allowing the gospel to address those needs, we have designed services and called everyone to come to us.

The corporate worship gathering is important, good, and right; but something is out of place when our focus on making them great diminishes our efforts in mission within the culture around us. It also tends to produce churches shaped by the cultural preferences of a few rather than indigenous responses of the people there as they come to know Christ as Lord.

That Isn't the Only Way ...

There is another way to plant churches, though; one that takes culture into the equation and results in churches that reflect that truth. Planting the gospel in a culture and allowing the culture to shape the churches as they grow within, not removed from, their culture will result in indigenous churches forming around those disciples. Our tendency toward "extractional" discipleship is a hindrance to the process.[80] A simple formula for planting indigenous churches might look like this:

planting the gospel in a culture
+
making disciples within the same culture
=
indigenous churches

It is possible for missionaries crossing cultures to plant indigenous churches, but it requires a humility often missing from the process. We need to learn to play second fiddle. In days gone by, plays would often feature a single fiddler on stage to accompany the action of the story. A second fiddler would be off-stage and unseen by the crowd who could play just as well as the one on stage. If the fiddler on stage broke a string, the back-up player would begin to play, and the on-stage player would mimic playing to keep up appearances. The crowd would be completely unaware that the second fiddler was there, and he would receive no recognition for the part he played.[81]

In regard to disciple-making, missionaries, in their own neighborhoods or completely new and foreign cultures would do well to practice playing second fiddle. Several years ago, missiologist David Garrison wrote *Church Planting Movements* based on research of church multiplication around the world and its underlying principals. In the book, he pointed out that missionaries should keep a low profile as they seek to initiate and nurture the movement. The missionary church planter should minimize foreignness and encourage indigeneity by mentoring pastors from behind the scenes.[82]

For those brought up in a Western culture that glorifies celebrity, even within our pulpits, it may be a difficult task to rethink and reorganize priorities enough to play second fiddle. Doing so, however, paves the way toward raising up indigenous leaders that will lead to indigenous local expressions of the church.

80 More on this in the "Engaging Tribes" Section, Week 8, Day 1.

81 "Where does the term second fiddle come from?" Wiki Answers Wiki.Answers.com, accessed May 15, 2012, http://wiki.answers.com/Q/where_does_the_term_second_fiddle_come_from. (Accessed November 2015)

82 David Garrison, *Church Planting Movements* (Richmond: International Mission Board, 1999), 17.

#	Homework due:__________
1	Think honestly about your local church. What is the priority for your church—not on paper, but by time, energy, and resources?
2	How can you (your church) focus more on making disciples? Be specific. How can these efforts lead to more indigenous churches?

#	Homework, cont.
3	What needs to change within your church to see these efforts come to fruition?
4	**Pray** for your church—particularly any ways that you have determined could be useful in making more disciples. Ask for wisdom and creativity as you humbly approach the culture around you with the gospel. Pray that you would see particular responses to the gospel that are specific to the people to whom you are sent.

Week Eleven: day 5

Shaping Leaders

Mission organizations have an acrostic for almost everything. One example that deals with raising up leaders is the acronym MAWL. Although it conjures up an image of a grizzly bear attack, it has a much subtler, kinder use in mission circles. The acronym defines the following approach to raising up leaders:

Model—Model for them how it should be done and spend time debriefing them in the process, including what and why you are doing what you do.
Assist—Let them do the work, and you help them as needed and provide real-time coaching.
Watch—Observe them as they lead and provide necessary feedback.
Leave—Identify another potential leader and repeat the process.[83]

Mission strategist and trainer Curtis Sergeant teaches that MAWL is the rhythm of discipleship that contributes to a Church Planting Movement (CPM). This model assists the missionary in training the new believer in planting CPM-oriented churches, watches to see that they and the churches are reproducing, and then leaves in order to begin the cycle over again. Sergeant relates the MAWL model to teaching a child to ride a bicycle, in that the parent "provides a model by riding the bicycle, provides assistance to the child by holding the bicycle as he learns to ride, then watches while the child rides the bicycle by himself, and finally leaves the child to ride on his own."[84]

Jesus appears to have espoused a similar model in the Gospels. He called the disciples to Himself, taught them, ministered alongside them, sent them out, and finally went away so they could accomplish greater things in His absence than they could with Him present (John 14:12; 16:7-11). The same is true for those who are working to disciple people and see indigenous expressions of the church rise up as a result. The missionary playing second fiddle and eventually even leaving the theater altogether is the most efficient way to see indigenous leaders trained while maintaining their cultural identity.

Another term used in church-planting movement strategy conversations is "exit strategy." The essence of this conversation has to do with how a missionary plans to effectively leave in order for the work to sustain, reproduce, and thrive. While sometimes this is actually a measurable

83 Ibid.

84 J. Guy Muse, "Model, Assist, Watch, Leave." *The M Blog*, July 2, 2007, accessed May 15, 2012, http://guymuse.blogspot.com/2007/07/model-assist-watch-leave.html

date set in the future, it often has more to do with what the missionary intentionally does and does not do, strategically, as he models his work, assists the new indigenous leader, and provides valuable insight or debriefing with the local leader.

Here again we see the need for humility and the reality of Jesus' teaching that our purpose is to serve (Mark 10:43-44). For the church on mission, leaving, or being left, is a reality as people are equipped and sent for the sake of the gospel. Rightly trained, they will be prepared to bring gospel transformation into their culture and make other disciples of their Lord.

#	Activity
1	The language may be a little different (maybe "send" instead of "leave"), but this principle certainly still applies not only in missionary work around the globe, but in training leaders for local missionary work/church planting. Write out your ideas about how your local church can make use of this training model:

Reproducibility

The ability of a church to reproduce itself is extremely important in seeing the gospel move to not yet believing people. Living organisms reproduce. Churches are living organisms and should multiply. We want to see churches that plant churches that plant churches. Mission strategists use a well-known tool to measure the reproducibility of the church called the "Three Self Formula."[85] This formula has been used for over 150 years and was first implemented by a pair of mission executives who headed the largest mission agencies of their day, Henry Venn and Rufus Anderson. It defines a mature/indigenous church as one that is self-governing, self-propagating, and self-supporting—the three selfs.

Missionary Douglas Hayward wrote that one of the attractive features of this formula was its simplicity. "Missionaries could actually count the number of pastors, evangelists, and church leaders who were operating under their own support systems, governing their own churches, and proclaiming the gospel to their own people. While it was easy if the missionary had accomplished his three-fold objective, the three-self formula did not really measure indigeneity. Its primary measurement was independence. Every trait of the three-self formula could be fully operational, but the church might, nevertheless, still be a foreign organization with an alien message".[86]

The church on mission must carefully evaluate the standards placed on its work in order to ensure reproducibility. In most cases, imported metrics are unrealistic, at best. David Garrison addressed the effects of imposing extra-biblical requirements for being a church:

> "When a mission, union or convention attempts to require a congregation to have extra-biblical things such as land, a building, seminary-trained leadership, or paid clergy before granting them full status as a church, a Church Planting Movement is obstructed. Christians may have the best of intentions when they impose preconditions before officially constituting a church—preconditions usually aimed at ensuring viability of the church before leaving it to its own devices. However, requirements such as building, property and salaried clergy quickly can become millstones around the neck of the church and make reproducing itself all the more unlikely".[87]

Two critical sticking points affect reproducibility among North American missionaries. First, there is too high a value placed on excellence. Often the excellence level sought by church leadership requires professionalism only attained by highly trained and highly paid staff. As a result, ministry opportunities that don't meet the extra-biblical requirements of excellence are cut, and gifted people without professional training are not equipped and used for the sake of the gospel.

The second sticking point is our over-indulgent pragmatism. Excellence and pragmatism are related in that as churches strive for excellence, they are constantly on the lookout for best practices, or other peoples' pragmatic approaches to whatever it is they are trying to accomplish. Too often, the result is a church or leadership that believes their way is the most effective and efficient, and their pragmatic approach is transferred into other contexts with no accommodation for cultural difference. This approach is irresponsible at best and dangerous at worst, and it does not engender reproducibility.

#	Question
1	Is your church reproducible? If so, where? If not, why not? What would it take to create a sustainable, reproducible model for your missionary endeavors both locally and globally?

Avoiding Dependency

Missionaries desire for the church to reproduce by itself, but often partnering churches give to the mission effort in an unhealthy way. Even when the church's intentions are perfectly honorable, supporting in the wrong manner develops dependency on outside resources and ends any hope of reproducibility of the newly planted work. Churches must prayerfully navigate the waters of partnership and support, including making decisions on providing resources. Providing these types of things is not always bad, but churches, in their zeal to serve and give, can very easily develop missionary efforts that are totally dependent on their support for survival. If the church is dependent upon outside support, then it is not indigenous, because it requires something not found in the local soil. Mutually beneficial partnerships are instead based on deeper connections such as common calling, shared vision and expectations, and mutual learning.

These five principles will help us as we develop the tradecraft of protecting indigeneity. We want to see the gospel advance unhindered by additional requirements from the ones who bring it. Protecting indigeneity will allow the church to grow and thrive planted firmly in its native soil.

#	Homework due:__________
1	Does your local church plant other churches? Why or why not?

#	Homework, cont.
2	Is there a model(s) you regularly use to do so? How do train leadership for those plants? How are they funded?
3	Do those plants meet the criterion of MAWL, reproducibility, and avoiding dependency? Should they all? If so, how could they be shaped in order to do so?

#	Homework, cont.
4	How do these principles apply to everyone within your church (all Christians are missionaries)?
5	**Pray** for those who are/will be raised up as leaders within your church to be sent out to plant churches. Pray for wisdom as you develop the strategy to send them.

Week Eleven: Questions for Group Discussion

#	Questions
1	What is indigeneity? As you did with the contextualization discussion, debate the issue—half of the group argues for its importance while the other half argues against it.
2	Is it a problem to have a church that looks and sounds just like your local body in a foreign culture? Why or why not?
3	Discuss your local church—is it an indigenous expression that bloomed from the soil in which it is planted? Or can you point out things within your worship that are imported? Are those things OK, or would it be useful to figure out how to change them?

#	Questions, cont.
4	Talk about your local mission efforts. If indigeneity is the result of well-contextualized discipleship in the gospel, are you seeing your mission efforts result in new indigenous expressions of the church locally?
5	Have the same conversation about your international efforts. Are you seeing indigenous expressions of the church in the wake of well-contextualized gospel effort?
6	Discuss how you raise and release leaders within your local body. Talk about how Jesus trained and sent disciples out. Do the two resemble one another? How so? How might they be different?

#	Questions, cont.
7	Are your local mission efforts reproducible, particularly for new believers to be trained to lead?
8	How are you training locals who come to faith in Christ to lead? Are your models reproducible? Are they dependent on outside resources? If so, should they be; how could you reshape that as a church?
9	What are your metrics for both local and international mission? How do those metrics affect raising up new leadership or reproducing churches? Could those metrics be shaped to better encourage reproducibility?

Week Twelve: Questions for Group Discussion

You have walked through nine different missionary skills and several other important ideas over the past 11 weeks. You have seen both biblical bases and the practical relationship of these skills to both local and global mission. All that remains is for you to begin to apply them. This week's discussion is simple—walk together through each of the skills and devise a plan for its implementation. Consider both individual implementation and implementation on the whole as a church.

#	Questions
1	1. Following the Spirit

#	Questions, cont.
2	2. Mapping
3	3. Exegeting culture

#	Questions, cont.
4	4. Building relationships
5	5. Persons of peace

#	Questions, cont.
6	6. Engaging tribes
7	7. Contextualization

#	Questions, cont.
8	8. Pursuing alternative pathsa
9	9. Protecting indigeneity

BIBLIOGRAPHY

Allen, Roland. Missionary Methods—St. Paul's or Ours? Cambridge: Lutterworth Press, 2006.

Bierlein, J.F. Parallel Myths. New York: Ballentine, 1994.

Blackaby, Henry. Experiencing God: Knowing and Doing the Will of God. Nashville: Broadman and Holman, 2008.

Booker, Christopher. The Seven Basic Plots: Why We Tell Stories. London: Continuum, 2005.

Bosch, David J. Transforming Mission: Paradigm Shifts in Theology of Mission. New York:Orbis, 1991.

Calvin, John. Institutes of the Christian Religion. Peabody: Hendrickson, 2007.

Coleman, Robert E. The Master Plan of Evangelism. Grand Rapids: Baker, 1963.

Crider, Caleb, Larry McCrary, Rodney Calfee, and Wade Stephens. Tradecraft: For the Church on Mission. Portland: Urban Loft, 2013.

Dodd, Patton. "A Better Storyteller: Donald Miller Helps Culturally Conflicted Evangelicals Make Peace With Their Faith." Christianity Today, June 2007. Accessed November 2015: http://www.christianitytoday. com/ct/2007/ june/10.28.html.

Erickson, Millard J. God in Three Persons: A Contemporary Interpretation of the Trinity. Grand Rapids: Baker, 1995.

Frost, Michael. Exiles: Living Missionally in a Post-Christian Culture. Grand Rapids: Baker, 2006.

Garrison, David. Church Planting Movements. Richmond: International Mission Board, 1999.

Godin, Seth. Tribes: We Need You To Lead Us. New York: Portfolio, 2008.

Henry, Matthew. "Complete Commentary on the Whole Bible: Luke 10." Study Light. Accessed September 2015: http://www.studylight.org/com/mhc-com/view.cgi?book=luchapter=010.

Hirsch, Alan and Lance Ford. Right Here Right Now: Everyday Mission For Everyday People.Grand Rapids: Baker, 2011.

Keller, Tim. Counterfeit Gods: The Empty Promises of Money, Sex, and Power, and the Only Hope That Matters. New York: Dutton, 2009.

Lai, Patrick. Tent-making: The Life and Work of Business as Missions. Colorado Springs: Biblical Publishing, 2005.

Larson, Donald. Guidelines for Barefoot Language Learning: An Approach Through Involvement and Independence. Minnesota: CMS, 1984.

Lloyd-Jones, David Martyn. The Sovereign Spirit: Discerning His Gifts. New York: Doubleday, 1994.

Lynch, Kevin. The Image of the City. Cambridge: M.I.T., 1960.

Muse, J. Guy. "Model, Assist, Watch, Leave." The M Blog, July 2, 2007. Accessed May 15, 2012, http://guymuse.blogspot.com/2007/07/model-assist-watch- leave.html

Myers, Joseph. The Search to Belong. Grand Rapids: Youth Specialties, 2003.

Newbigin, Lesslie. The Open Secret: An Introduction to the Theology of Missions. Grand Rapids: Eerdmans, 1978.

Stetzer, Ed. "Indigenous Church Planting." Church Planting Village. Accessed May 15, 2012:http://www.oklahomachurchplanting.com/wp-content/uploads/2012/12/Indigenous-Church-Planting.pdf.

Taber, Charles R. Exploring Church Growth. Grand Rapids: Eerdmans, 1983.

The International Mission Board. "Definition of a Church." January 25, 2005. Richmond, VA:http://www.imb.org/updates/storyview.aspx?StoryID=3838)

Vanderstelt, Jeff. "Why Throwing Parties is Missional." Verge Network. Accessed October 2015:http://www.vergenetwork.org/2012/02/10/why-throwing-parties-is-missional-jeff-vanderstelt/.

Vines, W.E. An Expository Dictionary of New Testament Words. Old Tappan, NJ: Fleming H. Revell Company, 1966.

Winter, Ralph. "The Highest Priority: Cross-Cultural Evangelism" (lecture at the International Congress on World Evangelization). Switzerland: 1974.

Winter, Ralph. "Unreached Peoples and Beyond (1974 to Now)," YouTube, last modified September 2015: http://youtube.com/watch?v=S8KBHqjld5k.

Wolf, Thomas A. "Oikos Evangelism: The Biblical Pattern." (Golden Gate Baptist Theological Seminary white paper). San Fransisco: 1999.

Wolf, Thomas A. "Persons of Peace." Accessed September 2015: http://www.kncsb.org/resources/PersonsofPeace.pdf.

Wolf, Thomas A. "The City" (lecture presented at Golden Gate Baptist Theological Seminary). San Francisco: 2000.

Wolf, Thomas A. "The Universal Discipleship Pattern." New Delhi: 1992. Accessed May 7, 2012:http://tinyurl.com/76n62bb.

Wolf, Thomas A. "Urban Social Change" (lecture presented at Golden Gate Baptist Theological Seminary). San Francisco: 1998.

Zannini, Paola "Five Tips for Growing Native Plants." Times Free Press, February 5, 2011. Accessed May 15, 2012: http://www.timesfreepress.com/news/2011/feb/05/5-tips-for-growing-native-plants/.

More from The Upstream Collective

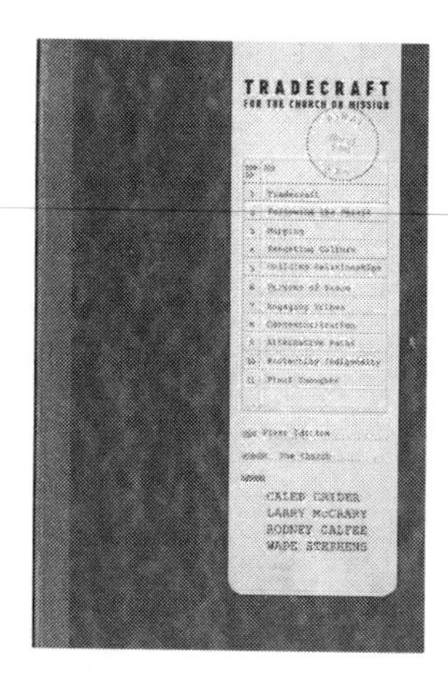

Tradecraft: For the Church on Mission
by Larry McCrary, Caleb Crider, Rodney Calfee, and Wade Stephens

The Western Church world is abuzz with talk of being missional. Church leaders, conference speakers, and authors are weighing the merits of the attractional church movement of the past few decades, and where they find it lacking, prescribing changes in the way we need to approach our cultures with the Gospel. There has been a consensus shift among many churches, networks, and denominations to become more focused on mission. The result is a renewed interest in reaching the lost in our cities and around the world. The Church, in many places in the Western world, is in fact returning to a biblical missional focus. Yet there is something still to be addressed in the process: the how. For centuries, God has called missionaries to cross cultures with the Gospel, and along the way, they have developed the necessary skill-sets for a cultural translation of the Good News. These skills need to be shared with the rest of the Church in order to help them as well be effective missionaries. Tradecraft: For the Church on Mission does exactly that. This book, in essence, pulls back the curtain on tools once accessible only to full-time Christian workers moving overseas, and offers them to anyone anywhere who desires to live missionally.

THE SENDING CHURCH DEFINED

The Sending Church Defined
by Zach Bradley

Purpose-driven church. Simple church. Organic church. Missional church. Deep church. Radical church. Transformational church. Total church. Sticky church. Tribal church. Mission-shaped church. Center church. Vertical church. Everyday church. Deliberate church. Gospel-centered church. Do we really need one more _________ church? "Yes!" says the collective of churches who consider themselves part of a growing movement called "sending church". It has proven itself as a term that is here to stay, but the meaning of it has been sadly mistaken. Many churches who call themselves sending churches are actually far from it. Some who are familiar with the term consider it just another missional trend. Others, upon first encounter think it speaks only to missiology. Sending church desperately needs clarity.That's precisely what this book is for. It began with a gathering of sending churches who sought to answer the question, "What is a sending church?" They came up with a lengthy definition, and we then took almost a year to flesh out that definition one word at a time according to Scripture and scholarship. The goal was not just clarity, but to send a timely word to churches about reclaiming their birthright as the leaders in the Great Commission.

First 30 Daze: Practical Encouragement for Living Abroad Intentionally by Larry and Susan McCrary

Being a part of a non-profit sector allows us to live in and travel to many cities in the United States, as well as in Europe. As followers of Jesus, wherever we live or travel, our goal is to live out our faith in a different culture. It does not matter if you are a full-time vocational Christian worker, an international company employee, a student studying abroad, or a person who simply wants to live and work in another country—the first 30 days matter! The sooner that you can get out the door, learn the culture, meet people, build relationships, and discover what God has in store for you, the sooner you will feel at home and love your new environment. Thirty topics and Scripture verses are introduced as well as practical ways to apply what you've learned each day through a simple but fun application assignment. You may want to use the book as an individual devotional, with your family, or with a group. Regardless, it is short and practical so that you have plenty of time to get out and enjoy your new home.

Order in bulk and get bulk pricing at theupstreamcollective.org/books
For more resources, training, and consulting to empower local churches on mission, visit theupstreamcollective.org

Made in the USA
Columbia, SC
06 September 2017